Bris Milah

Endpapers: *A mohel's instrument box, of painted wood, the top decorated with a circumcision scene. (Italy, 18th century)*

ברית מילה

HENRY C. ROMBERG MD

Bris Milah

A BOOK ABOUT THE JEWISH RITUAL OF CIRCUMCISION

FELDHEIM PUBLISHERS
Jerusalem / New York

Picture credits and sources

Endpapers: from the collection of Dr Michael Kaniel, Jerusalem
pp. 16, 73: Ets Haim Library, Amsterdam (Jewish National and University Library, Jerusalem)
pp. 36, 37, 108: Jewish National and University Library, Jerusalem
p. 45: The Jewish Museum, London (Keter Publishing House, Jerusalem)
pp. 47 (upper), 49, 116, 142: Israel Museum, Jerusalem
pp. 47 (lower), 51, 52, 58: Rabbi David Epstein (Shlomo Marcus), Jerusalem
pp. 100, 112-113, 133: Israel Museum (David Harris), Jerusalem
pp. 176-177: MS 601/1, the Klau Library, Hebrew Union College - Jewish Institute of Religion, Cincinnati (JNUL)
p. 192: Moriah Art-Craft, New York (Keter Publishing House, Jerusalem)

First published 1982
ISBN 0-87306-290-6

Phototypeset at the Feldheim Press

Philipp Feldheim Inc.
96 East Broadway
New York, NY 10002

Feldheim Publishers Ltd
POB 6525 / Jerusalem, Israel

Printed in Israel

In honor of the fiftieth wedding anniversary
of Rabbi and Mrs. M.M.S.

The child being brought into the synagogue, where the mohel stands ready: Oil painting by Moritz Oppenheimer, from 19th-century Germany.

Foreword

Everyone likes to attend a *bris milah* (ritual circumcision). I have noticed that no one is ever bored or uninterested at such an occasion. Indeed, many are deeply affected by the ceremony they are witnessing and are eager to learn more about what is happening.

One of the great pleasures I have when I am invited to perform a bris milah is the opportunity to explain some of the details of the procedure and its background in Jewish history. Many people have not had the chance in the course of their own Jewish education to learn about these matters and, indeed, many observant Jews are themselves quite uninformed about some aspects of this particular *mitzvah* (commandment). Yet all would agree that bris milah is certainly a precept which has always occupied a central place in Jewish life.

I have written this short book, drawing on my years of experience as a *mohel* and as a teacher of this subject to lay audiences in the Cleveland area, to enable my fellow Jews to gain a broader and deeper understanding of ritual circumcision—bris milah. Many chapters will be of interest to parents who are expecting a new addition to the family or who have just welcomed a newborn boy into the world. Other chapters will be primarily of interest to other *mohalim* (performers of ritual circumcision). Most practitioners of this art are constantly learning from one another and are always discussing techniques and problems.

But most of all, I hope and pray, this book will be of interest to the general Jewish reader who is moved to learn more of the history, traditions, and practices of his people. I have directed the main thrust of my writing to this last group.

ACKNOWLEDGMENTS

In addition to the persons mentioned in the text, I want to thank the following people for their contributions to my work as a mohel and to the writing of this book:

Rabbi Yehuda Blum, the *rav* of Congregation *K'hal Yereim*, Cleveland Heights, Ohio, who reviewed the text for halachic accuracy (though I take full responsibility for any errors which may have slipped through unnoticed). Rabbi Blum has been the final word in the many halachic questions which I have brought to him during my years as a mohel.

Rabbi Avraham Chaim Feuer, author of the ArtScroll Tehillim series, who has critically reviewed the text of this volume. In addition, Rabbi Feuer has offered repeated encouragement to me to finish this book at times when other obligations and interests kept taking me away from the long and difficult task of writing.

Rabbi Mordecai Gifter, *rosh hayeshivah* of Yeshivas Telshe—Cleveland and of Yeshivas Telshe-Stone in Israel, who carefully read the manuscript and appended his kind thoughts to this publication. Over the years, Rabbi Gifter's constant encouragement not only of me but of the entire Jewish community has resulted in an elevation of standards both of learning and practice.

Rabbi Irving Grumer, the *rav* of Congregation *Oer Chodosh Anshe Sfard* of University Heights, Ohio, who has answered halachic questions about milah on many occasions and whose tireless efforts in the area of Jewish divorce have raised community standards in this vital area of Jewish life.

The heirs of Rabbi Eliyahu Kitov, of blessed memory, for giving us permission to include the chapter on Bris Milah from his work *Ish u'Beyso*.

Moshe Halevi Spero, accomplished author and scholar who is well known for his work in the interface between Judaism and psychology, who carefully proofread the manuscript and made numerous corrections and suggestions which were incorporated into the final form which the book assumed.

All the mohalim who have taught me both by their own selfless interest in my developing skills and by the superlative personal examples which their own lives and approach to Judaism offer to the entire community.

My devoted wife, Rochel Esther, whose encouragement and interest in every *d'var mitzvah* are directly responsible for this book. And her parents, Shmuel Yitzchok and Bas-Sheva Goldish of Tulsa, Oklahoma, for raising such a fine Jewish daughter.

And finally my Rebbe (the Lubavitcher Rebbe), Rabbi Menachem Mendel Schneerson *shlita*, a true Jewish leader, who not only provides direction to the entire Jewish people but who takes personal interest in each and every Jew. When I first began writing a few years ago, I expressed to him my concern that such activities were *bitul z'man* and *bitul Torah*. He strongly disagreed, stating that through writing I would be more able to spread the knowledge of Torah to the Jewish people. I hope that this book will achieve success in this direction.

Contents

Introduction

THE CRYING INFANT is brought into the living room, which is crowded now with relatives and guests. There is a flurry of activity which you have a hard time following. The mohel is saying a few prayers in Hebrew which you do not understand and then, leaning over the infant, performs an operation which you know is a circumcision. But you cannot see too well from the back of the room where you're standing. The infant is then wrapped up and handed to someone while the mohel fills a silver goblet with wine and says some more Hebrew prayers. He pauses in the ceremony and gives the infant a sip of wine. Suddenly, it is all over and everyone is saying *mazal tov.*

This is a bris milah, a ritual circumcision. Though you really do not understand everything that has just happened, you share in the joy and happiness of the occasion, realizing that something very Jewish has just occurred. Perhaps you have that fleeting sensation of inner hunger (it's there in all of us) to know more about the heritage of our people, to experience a deeper involvement in the destiny of our nation. You want to know more. You wish you had had a better Jewish education.

When I am asked to officiate as the mohel at a bris, I try to make it not only a wonderful *simchah* (happy occasion of religious significance) for all concerned, but also a learning experience for those friends and guests who may not know what is going on. I usually explain every aspect of the ritual and mention the traditions associated with different parts of the performance. For example: What is the Chair of Elijah? What is its source in Jewish tradition? After the bris, I make myself available to answer questions for any interested persons. I frequently find myself staying an hour longer than I had planned, as everyone wants to know more. In fact, at a bris I have never met a Jew who displayed the "so what" attitude so often encountered when you start talking to him about going more regularly to synagogue or being more careful with his standards of *kashrus* (Jewish dietary law).

The fact is that I am often left with a terrible sense of inadequacy after I leave a home where I have just performed a bris. There is always so much more to say, so many questions left unanswered. I wonder: Did I present the many small nuggets of Jewish information in a form that will be remembered and possibly be transformed someday into practice? Certainly a kosher (valid) bris was performed, an eternal covenant renewed between the Jewish people and the Almighty. Nothing can change that. But how well did

I convey the meaning of the ceremony, its history and traditions to the Jews who were there?

These persistent doubts are the main reason for this small book: It is a response to the tremendous thirst for Jewish knowledge I continually meet whenever I talk with fellow-Jews.

There is remarkably little written in the English language about ritual circumcision, and what has been written is woefully inadequate for the needs of today's questioning American Jew. It is said that there are seventy facets to Torah: that is, seventy different but complementary explanations to every aspect of Jewish life. In one age, certain points of view are more easily understood; in yet another age, other points of view make a more lasting impression and stimulate the desire to learn. All such approaches are authentic, but some are more readily accepted, depending upon the time, the country, and the background of the listener.

In this book, I am writing to the average American Jew, a composite of the thousands of men and women I have met at bris milah ceremonies. My hope is that through this book I will be successful in conveying thoughts and ideas, explanations and understandings which I have not had time enough to clearly explain during the performance of an actual bris — and to far more people than I shall have met in my own personal career. This is perhaps the purpose of the book that the Lubavitcher Rebbe had in mind when he encouraged me to write it, and I can only hope and pray that it will "do the job."

The title-page of a mohel's book (manuscript), in which he recorded the names of those he circumcised (1724-1760). As his name was Shlomo, two pictures relate to King Solomon (bottom center: his judgment of the two women's dispute over the living child). The other pictures refer to circumcision. Upper right: Elijah's chair; lower left: the child being taken from the mother for the bris; lower right: the circumcision. (Ets Haim Library, Amsterdam)

1

Do we need another mohel in town?

MY OWN INVOLVEMENT in bris milah came about in a rather round-about way. I had always been bothered by the fact that the majority of Jewish boys born in Cleveland were circumcised by a doctor in the hospital in a routine surgical fashion on the first or second day of life. These children were actually being deprived of a cardinal mitzvah in Jewish life. Moreover, their parents were usually too far removed from traditional Jewish living to even appreciate this deficiency.

At the time, I was not in a position to intervene directly, so I composed a letter to the *Cleveland Jewish News* and persuaded nine of my medical colleagues to sign it with me—thinking that perhaps a *minyan* of physicians might make some impression on the Jewish community of Cleveland.

The letter, which the newspaper published, read as follows:

We feel, as Jewish physicians, that a few words have to be forthrightly spoken about an aspect of Jewish life which transcends the ideological differences between the Orthodox, Conservative and Reform groups in American Judaism.

This is bris milah (circumcision), which has been the practice of our people for 4,000 years. This is a precept so ancient and so ingrained in the subconscious of our nation that, until recently, it would have been unthinkable to omit a properly performed bris to initiate a male Jewish infant into the Covenant of Abraham.

Yet, today, mainly because many young Jewish parents do not know what a bris is, infants are being circumcised by physicians who are well-meaning, but untrained in the proper ritual and method of bris milah.

It is important to stress that a circumcision such as is done on a non-Jewish baby for sound medical and hygienic reasons is not the same as a bris milah. Not only is the surgical procedure itself different, but a bris is *never* done before the eighth day of life.

In addition, the bris is usually attended by the child's parents in their own house, with grandparents, friends, and relatives all enjoying the little celebration given in honor of the new arrival.

Any Jewish parents who are expecting a new addition to their family should feel free to call any of the undersigned for further information. Speakers, rabbinical or medical, can be arranged for temple groups.

Signed,
Etc.

A letter written, my conscience was appeased, and the matter was forgotten — but not for long. A curious set of occurrences set me again to thinking of a more personal involvement with the mitzvah of bris milah.

For reasons known only to themselves, the rulers of the Soviet Union, an empire in the fullest sense of the term, whose territories stretch from Central Europe to the furthest reaches of the Far East, from the coldest shores of the Arctic Ocean to the tropical depths of Central Asia, decided to allow large numbers of Jews to emigrate and take up residence in the free world. Though the Soviet motives were unclear, the result of this new government policy resulted in tens of thousands of Jews being able to leave the confines of Russia to settle elsewhere. Large numbers eventually found their way to the United States.

The saga of this emigration is a book in itself. However, one fact relating to my own involvement with bris milah is that hundreds started to come to Cleveland. From the arrival of the first families, I began to work with the *Neshei Chabad* organization and its president, Mrs. Zalman Kazen, who from the start was deeply involved in the resettlement of Russian Jews in Cleveland. We wanted to introduce (or reintroduce) these new arrivals to some meaningful concept of traditional Judaism. This was no small task, as most of these newcomers were already two generations removed from any kind of Jewish practice. Sixty years of Communist anti-religious propaganda had clearly had its effect.

However, the new Russian immigrants responded

very quickly to one particular area of Torah observance: bris milah. For the past twenty years in the Soviet Union, most Jews had not been able to obtain circumcision, ritual or otherwise, for their sons, the result being that almost all Jewish emigrants from Russia under the age of twenty or thirty are uncircumcised. The *Neshei Chabad* "Russian Project" undertook to send Russian Jewish males to New York, where ritual circumcision could be arranged, since no such facilities were available at that time in Cleveland. The expense was great, for not only was it necessary to send the individual to New York and pay for his living expenses, hospital, and other costs, but the mother of the child also had to accompany him. Something had to be done.

Previously, two men for whom I held the greatest respect had urged me to learn milah. Rabbi Moshe Hildeshaim (may he be remembered for a blessing), who has since passed away, was highly regarded by everyone in our community. His advice was sought not only because he was a great *talmid chochom* (a title reserved for those few in a Jewish community who are thoroughly versed in Talmud and in Jewish law) but also because his character and human qualities were so highly developed that he served as a model of Jewish behavior. He urged me to learn and practice as a mohel. My good friend and partner in daily Talmud studies, Rabbi Moshe Reuven Barkin, may he live and be well, also strongly urged me in this direction, because he felt the practice of milah in Cleveland needed strengthening.

Ultimately, for many reasons—not the least of which was the arrival of so many Russians who needed ritual circumcision—I began to reconsider the matter of bris milah in a more personal way.

At Mrs. Kazen's urging and with her encouragement, I wrote a letter asking the advice of my teacher and guide, the Lubavitcher Rebbe.

The answer came a few days later. Rabbi Leibel Groner, the Rebbe's secretary, telephoned to inform me that the Rebbe replied that I should learn both adult and infant milah, and that I should be blessed in the performance of this mitzvah with *hatzlachah* (success).

It might seem unusual that a physician, quite confident in his abilities as a doctor and highly trained in the medical arts and sciences, should hesitate to learn an apparently simple surgical procedure without the permission and encouragement of a rabbi. Perhaps a review of the role of the Jewish leader in the life of a Jew would be enlightening for those not of Orthodox Jewish background.

The concept of Jewish leadership is quite old, dating back to the time of Abraham, the first Jew. Yet, it is an institution which in modern times has been quite misunderstood, since the criteria for assuming leadership within the Jewish community have changed considerably, especially among those who have lost their traditions. Today, leadership for some comes with personal wealth. This is frequently seen in the leadership hierarchy of Jewish Federation circles where "money talks." For others, leadership is seen as a wholly political matter, in terms of influence peddling, political debts, and majority rule. Thus, it is quite possible for a person to be a leader in the American Jewish community even though he is married to a non-Jewish woman or is less than scrupulous in his business dealings. It is equally possible, following such an interpretation of leadership, that a person be an influential rabbi though having never opened the *Code of Jewish Law* or a *Gemara* since his long-forgotten seminary days.

Until relatively recent times, however, Jewish leadership has been correctly characterized by excellence in all areas of Jewish life. A Jewish leader is a person who best represents the highest and finest ideals and aspirations of the Jewish nation. A Jewish leader is not only outstanding in his understanding and mastery of the Jewish law, but is a living example of Jewish tradition and observance. He not only is a master of common sense but is also wise in the psychology of man and in the fundamental truths of the world. One learns from a Jewish leader not only by what he says and teaches, but also by observing the way he talks, acts, and dresses. There is no defect in his intellectual or moral makeup.

All Orthodox Jews have a *rebbe*, by whatever name they choose to call him. For many he is a congregational rabbi. For others he is a *rosh yeshivah*, the head of a rabbinical college. For *chassidim*, he is the *Rebbe*, the leader of an extended family of men, women, and children to which he belongs. For Lubavitcher Chassidim, who number in the hundreds of thousands, he is the Lubavitcher Rebbe, seventh in descent from the great founder of the Lubavitcher or Chabad dynasty, the *Alter Rebbe* — Rabbi Schneur Zalman of Liadi.

A *chossid* does not undertake any major step in life, be it marriage, buying a house, or starting out in a new business, without first consulting the *Rebbe* for his advice and blessing. The *chossid* knows that the *Rebbe*'s answer will be useful and correct since he believes that the *Rebbe* has far greater experience and knowledge than he, and that the *Rebbe* is much closer to the Source of all good advice than the individual will ever be.

Therefore, it was logical that I should consult my Rebbe about embarking on the very serious and important business of becoming a mohel. Indeed, his blessing carried me through many trying times in this endeavor, since more than once the thought entered my mind that it would have been much simpler and much less stressful if I had never take up milah in the first place.

Now that permission had been granted and encouragement offered, the critical step was up to me. Although, as a physician, I was familiar with some of the basic aspects of this surgery since I had performed several circumcisions as a medical student, I now had to refine and adjust my techniques along traditional lines and become familiar with the laws, traditions, and ritual details of the procedure.

I would have to go to New York for more training.

2

Off to New York

THE AMERICAN AIRLINES JET had begun its descent over New York's La Guardia airport. It was a rainy Monday morning, one week and a half before Passover, and I was looking forward, not without a little apprehension, to meeting a number of mohalim who had agreed to teach me ritual circumcision.

I recalled my first exposure to circumcision as a medical student engaged in my required pediatrics rotation. The resident in charge of my education took me to the newborn service with him—he was scheduled to circumcise a number of infants that morning and wanted to show me how. After demonstrating the technique on one loudly screaming baby, he said to me, "Here the principle is, 'You see one; you do one; you teach one.'" He was, of course, alluding to the on-the-job-training of students on his service. I had just 'seen one' and he was now inviting me to 'do one'!

Gingerly, and under his close guidance, I 'did one.' We were using the Gomco Clamp, an unwieldy metal instrument, which first requires a dorsal incision of the foreskin and then the insertion of the Gomco device under and over the divided foreskin. The excess skin is then trimmed away and the Gomco Clamp removed. Using this clamp was supposed to allow for a bloodless procedure, but it was far from that in my unskilled hands. The baby was screaming, I was sweating profusely, and my resident was in a hurry. Nevertheless, the patient and the circumcisor survived and another (non-Jewish) male could now enjoy the many alleged pleasures and protections of the circumcised state.

Yet, merely knowing about the Gomco Clamp — I'd long since become rusty in the use of this instrument, not having handled one since my medical student years—is a far cry from being knowledgeable in the traditional techniques of ritual circumcision. For this, I had to fly to New York and learn personally from experienced mohalim.

It was not so simple to find someone willing to teach me. One mohel after another told Rabbi Barkin that he had *a kabolleh foon taten*, a tradition from his father, not to teach milah to a physician. My good friend Rabbi Barkin had to speak to many mohalim before Rabbi Katzenstein of Washington Heights agreed to initiate me into this honored profession.

This sentiment, that doctors should not be performing ritual circumcision, is very understandable since the institution of bris milah has become so confused in the minds of the American Jewish public with the surgical procedure of circumcision that the uniquely Jewish aspects of this Divinely instituted commandment are being forgotten. And, according to many, if doctors become conspicuous as ritual circumcisors, this confusion would be all the more increased.

I have always kept this sensitivity in mind and take great pains to ensure that people do not confuse bris milah with the minor operative procedure called circumcision. I take seriously the doubts and fears of their fathers. Even when performing a bris in the hospital I wear my *gartel* and large *tallis*. I insist on using a *sandek* and include all the details of my standard bris milah ceremony—rather than performing the bris behind a glass partition with a nurse holding the baby, the procedure in the so-called Ritual Rooms of many Jewish hospitals.

Nonetheless, I was still concerned with the propriety of a physician becoming a mohel and mentioned this point in my letter to the Lubavitcher Rebbe. He surely also took it into consideration in giving me the go-ahead. Actually, not so many centuries ago, the community Jewish physician was often the mohel. Rashi, the well-known 11th century commentator on the Bible and Talmud, refers to a physician who was a city's mohel (*Pesachim* 7b).

While on the subject, I must lay some of the blame for the confusion between bris milah and medical circumcision at the doorstep of some of my fellow mohalim. Unfortunately, too many mohalim feel that they enhance the status of milah by trying to act more the role of a medical practitioner than that of the religious functionary. They use medical jargon when talking with parents. Some will wear a doctor's smock during the bris. A number of traditional mohalim will even don surgeons' rubber gloves! No wonder there is confusion.

On the other hand, I know for a fact that many kosher ritual circumcisions have been performed which would not have been done had I not been available. These were cases of infants whose parents had planned to have circumcision done in the hospital by their doctor but were persuaded to go the more traditional route by family or friends. Having a doctor who is also a mohel had induced many young couples to have a ritual circumcision performed on their offspring. It is truly unfortunate that Jewish people have wandered so far from their spiritual origins that they feel more secure when the mohel is also a doctor. Nevertheless, facts are facts. However, I must stress that the traditional mohel performs a circumcision far more skillfully, far less traumatically, far more safely, and certainly far more aesthetically (though this last quality is in the eye of the beholder) than the average medical house officer who is assigned to circumcise newborn babies.

With these and other thoughts on my mind, I was sitting buckled in my seat on the American Airlines plane heading for the center of American Jewish life, New York City.

At La Guardia I called my first mohel, Rabbi

Edwin Katzenstein, a graduate of Cleveland's famed Telshe Yeshiva, who lives in Manhattan. His wife answered the phone and told me they were expecting me and to come right over. Incidentally, she also informed me that I would be their house guest in New York for as long as I cared to stay. I thanked her sincerely because I knew how busy she must be with Passover little more than a week ahead. I took a cab from the airport and arrived at the Katzensteins' apartment in less than twenty minutes.

If I might digress a moment, I would mention another great mitzvah which one can truly appreciate only when one experiences it oneself. It is *hachnossas orchim* or "welcoming guests." Although an observant Jew knows that a mitzvah is observed primarily because God so commands, some mitzvos are easier than others to understand logically. It is a great mitzvah to welcome visitors from other cities or even from other parts of one's own city. Such a visitor is treated as a member of the family and afforded every opportunity to enjoy a restful and stress-free stay at the house of his host. When the guest leaves, the host accompanies him as far as is possible to assure that he will get safely to his next destination.

Such noble hospitality was first demonstrated by Abraham, the father of the Jewish people. You will recall the story of the three angels who visited him just before the destruction of Sodom. To Abraham, they appeared as human travellers in need of a rest from the rigors of the road. Even though he himself was in considerable discomfort since he had undergone his own circumcision several days before, he left his tent and went out to welcome these weary men. He made them comfortable, fed them, and sent them on their way.

This characteristic of hospitality is a trademark of all of Abraham's descendants. Even the Arabs, who are descended from Ishmael, Abraham's oldest son, are reputed to this day to practice it. Among Jewish people, hospitality is a Divinely instituted commandment.

Like many homes in Cleveland Heights, ours has always been open to visitors. Not only do my wife and I enjoy meeting people from other parts of the country or world, but my children have benefitted greatly from their contacts with rabbis from Jerusalem, students from the nearby college campus, and many others who come to Cleveland for business or pleasure. But there are aspects of this mitzvah which I did not fully understand until I found myself the recipient of its benefits.

Coming without my wife and children to an unfamiliar part of New York, I was lonely indeed. In addition, I carried the burden of my apprehensions about learning a new skill and meeting many new people on unfamiliar territory. One can imagine how grateful I was to receive the Katzensteins' gracious offer.

3

My apprenticeship

Before I left for my apprenticeship in New York, I read everything available in English about bris milah. There really was not much published concerning the laws and traditions of the Jewish ritual practice, though the medical literature, particularly in the area of urology and pediatrics, contained many references.

The opinion of the medical profession itself is divided over the whole topic of circumcision. One group feels quite strongly that routine circumcision for all males is a good prophylactic health measure; the other group maintains with equal vigor that it is unnecessary, possibly dangerous, cosmetic surgery not accompanied by any proven or tangible benefit. Both sides concede, however, that as an ancient Jewish religious ritual, it need not be interfered with. This is stated plainly even by those who are most opposed to routine circumcision.

However, every so often articles which are openly

hostile to the Jewish practice of bris milah appear in the medical literature. These are usually written by assimilated Jews who are somewhat embarrassed by this "prehistoric remnant" of traditional Jewish life. Their total ignorance of their heritage is often quite obvious from the many inaccurate statements they include in the course of their writings.

One author (*Archives of Pediatrics*, 1951) suggests that the surgical technique might be improved by having the "patient's family . . . engage a rabbi of their choice in order that he may officiate in accordance with custom and tradition at the same time that the doctor is performing the surgery."

This same author goes on to defend this marked departure from tradition by claiming that Judaism is flexible and that other changes have been condoned. He declares, for example, that the "Mosaic Dietary Law is another very important law to be observed in Judaism, and as everyone knows, many of our best Jewish families enjoy pork chops and Virginia ham in their menus. Our religious leaders apparently do not disapprove of the infractions of the above laws." So much for his understanding of pork chop Judaism.

Another Jewish physician (*Clinical Pediatrics*, October 1962), after a long description of how unskilled and poorly qualified traditional mohalim are, admits that "ritual circumcision among Jews will probably continue for many generations" and suggests that "physicians teach parents that it is safer for the child if the operation be performed by a well trained surgeon and the liturgy recited by a rabbi or cantor." (His article on "ritual circumcision" is amply illustrated with three medieval paintings of the circumcision of the infant Jesus!)

Though my perusal of the medical literature was not too productive in terms of learning anything concrete about the ritual procedure of a traditional bris milah, discussion with friends and a reading of Jewish sources enabled me to formulate a series of questions I knew I would want answered during my visit to New York and in the course of my discussions with several mohalim with whom Rabbi Barkin had made appointments for me.

I composed a list of questions which I asked each of the six mohalim with whom I actually had the opportunity to talk. These queries concerned the examination of the baby before the bris, various problems that might be associated with certain aspects of the performance of the milah itself, such as the *priah* (tearing of the mucous membrane which lies under the foreskin) or the *metzitzah* (the sucking of blood from the wound after the foreskin has been removed). I also had some questions about *hatofas dam bris*, a compensatory ritual which is done when a Jewish male has already been circumcised by a doctor but not in a ritually acceptable manner. Also, there were some very simple but practical matters which I had to know—such as, for example: what does the mohel do with the foreskin after the circumcision? And, finally, I had to find out where I could purchase a set of instruments.

I am afraid that with my long list of questions I put

my newly-made friends through somewhat of a "third degree," but I am a methodical person and could not let this golden opportunity pass by. Probably because of my medical training, I did not find the technical aspects of the surgical procedure at all hard to learn. I was determined, however, to develop skills in the non-surgical facets of the ritual since this was all quite new to me. In addition, I was already convinced that the religious nature of bris milah had to be emphasized since, in modern American Jewish life, the whole procedure was coming to be regarded as a hygienic matter, as prophylaxis against disease, or perhaps at best, as an expression of ethnic identity.

This unfortunate disassociation of circumcision from its religious origins is probably also partially the fault of many mohalim who, responding defensively to charges of being improperly trained in what is rapidly becoming considered merely a surgical procedure, have begun to emphasize their medical know-how and familiarity with proper surgical procedure and appearance. Thus, as I have mentioned before, it is not uncommon to see mohalim garbed in hospital gowns or white physicians' jackets, wearing sterile rubber surgical gloves and face masks, totally abandoning the traditional instruments of their profession and relegating the ritual to a few rapidly pronounced Hebrew prayers and blessings.

I was impressed with Rabbi Katzenstein's technical knowledge of his subject. Not only was he thoroughly conversant with the normal anatomy of the male genitalia, but he was aware of various abnormalities which would require urological consultation. His understanding of asepsis and his knowledge of hemostatic technique were also impressive. I was not surprised to hear that he had completed a two-year course of instruction offered to mohalim by the Mount Sinai Hospital of New York even though he had been practicing milah for many years before he took this course of study.

There are only two schools in the world where the art and skill of milah are taught in any way resembling a standardized academic curriculum. One of these schools is in Great Britain, the other at the Mount Sinai Hospital of New York. The first class started in this institution in March of 1968 and its seven students graduated from the two year course of part time instruction in February 1970. A second class began its instruction in February 1971 and graduated in June 1972 (ten students), the course of study having been shortened to one and a half years. Since then, there have been no further courses offered since it was felt there was already a surplus of skilled mohalim in the New York area.

It should be pointed out that many mohalim feel strongly that such formal courses of instruction in a hospital setting should only supplement and not replace the traditional apprenticeship. Indeed, by the time Rabbi Katzenstein had enrolled in this rather unique school, he had already been a very busy mohel for many years. Nonetheless, he felt it was necessary for him to increase his expertise and competence—a desire quite in keeping with his general striving for excellence in everything he does. Traditionally, however, the mohel learns his craft not in any formal setting, but as an apprentice to a practicing mohel.

To be accepted as an apprentice, the candidate must be of sterling character, be personally observant of all the laws, customs, and traditions of halachic Jewish life, and be learned in the laws and methods of Torah study. Needless to say, he must have a steady hand, a keen eye, and a large share of common sense.

The author of *Yalkut Me-Am Lo'ez*, Rabbi Yaakov Culi, the well-known Sephardic commentator of the Bible who wrote in the early 18th century, describes the standards of training established over two centuries ago by the rabbinate of Constantinople:

> If a man wishes to learn milah, he must apprentice himself to an expert mohel for six months. He must accompany this mohel to all the brissim that he performs, gaining experience and learning all details. During these six months, he may not even touch the infant; he may only watch. After six months, he is permitted to bandage the child, but nothing else. Before being allowed to perform a bris, he must apprentice for a full two years. Then he must receive certification from the three most expert mohalim in the community. Even when an apprentice claims that he has completed the required two year course, his word is not accepted. He must have a written certification from the most expert mohalim. Without such a certification, he may not touch a child, even to examine him.

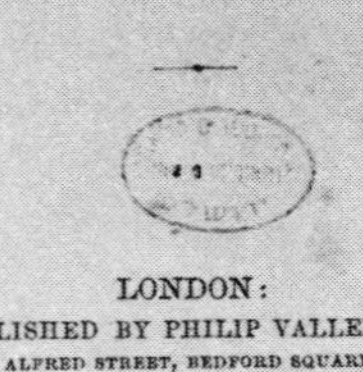

JEWISH

RITE OF CIRCUMCISION,

WITH THE

PRAYERS AND LAWS APPERTAINING THERETO.

Translated into English,

WITH AN INTRODUCTORY ESSAY,

BY

ASHER ASHER, M.D.

LONDON:
PUBLISHED BY PHILIP VALLENTINE,
34, ALFRED STREET, BEDFORD SQUARE, W.C.
5633—1873.

כפי מנהגי בני ספרד אשכנז ופולין יצ״ו
עם כל הדינים הנלוים אליו

מסודר ומתורגם ללשון איננליש

הרופא אשר בלא״א כ״ה פינחס זללה״ה

לונדון

שנת הִנה אנכי כורת ברית לפ״ג

לונדון
נדפס ע״י ווערטהיימר
בשנת תרל״ג לפ״ק

The text and laws of the bris, prepared and translated by Scotland's first Jewish physician, who was active afterward in London's Jewish life. Published in 1873 and reprinted many times in later decades.

METHODS

TO BE EMPLOYED BY MOHELIM

IN THE

PERFORMANCE OF CIRCUMCISION

AS RECOMMENDED BY

The Medical Members

of The Milah Board

OF THE KEHILLAH.

PRESS OF A. H. ROSENBERG, 131 HENRY ST, NEW YORK.

ספר הברית

מעט דברים נמרצים, מועילים ונחוצים, ככוכבים

מתנוצצים, דברי הרבנים, אשר בועד המילה

נמנים, בדבר מילת הבנים.

ווי איך נויטינג מעטהאדען וואס יעדער מוהל מוז וויסען ווי

זיך אויף צו פיהרען בעת דורך פיהרען די אפעראציאן

פון מילה, פון די דאקטוירים סטאף פון ועד המילה.

מאת ועד המילה שנתיסד מהקהלה דנוא יארק.

ונערך ע״י הרב ר׳ יעקב איסקאלסקי

בחדש ניסן התרע״ה.

בהוצאת הקהלה דנוא יארק.

בדפוס א. ח. ראזענבערג 131 הענרי סט. נוּיארק.

Yiddish and English title-pages of a booklet issued in 1915 by the Kehillah of New York, that contains standards and rules set by the rabbinic and medical members of the Kehillah's milah board.

In some New York and Israeli communities, certain specified standards are still in force, but this is not universally true. The high degree of competence which I have found in every mohel I have met and watched in action is undoubtedly due to the personal interest and detailed instruction which each man had received as an apprentice from his teacher.

The last thing which the observant Jewish community desires is governmental licensing since this often degenerates into a not so subtle ruse through which to eliminate traditional norms of bris milah and convert it into an aseptic, cosmetic, standardized surgical procedure totally devoid of religious meaning and value. Such governmental regulation would ultimately result in a doctor performing the surgical procedure and a rabbi or cantor saying the blessings and chanting the liturgy—a totally worthless exercise in the eyes of Jewish law. The next step might be to outlaw milah altogether, which unfortunately has happened at times throughout Jewish history.

The Jewish community must regulate itself. Certification should be given only to mohalim of proven competence who are willing to subject their practices to the scrutiny of the *Gedolei Torah*, the Torah leaders of the generation. In addition, it is incumbent upon all congregational rabbis to be acquainted with the standards of milah in their communities and the qualifications and skills of mohalim who are practicing in their regions so that they may advise young parents on the status or competence of local mohalim.

Needless to say, every mohel must continually study and review the extensive Jewish literature regarding his profession. In addition, consultations with other mohalim concerning technique, standards of hygiene, and potential halachic or technical problems should be the rule rather than the exception. Some mohalim attend professional meetings which are held in New York every few years.

There are many people, such as the irreligious Jewish physicians quoted earlier in the chapter, who are waiting for the opportunity to eliminate the traditional practice of bris milah. Many hospitals have already succeeded in turning this sacred rite into a surgical procedure completely devoid of Jewish meaning. This assimilationist point of view can be fought only through educating the Jewish people about the sacredness of this precious mitzvah and having the mohalim themselves embody the highest standards of piety, skill, and learning. Every bris a mohel is privileged to do, especially for families who have not been fortunate to have good Jewish education or traditional family upbringing, should be a learning experience for all those invited to the ceremony. The mohel will find that if he explains the traditions and customs, the laws as well as the reasons for what he is doing, his every word will make a deep impression on his listeners. He will have forged another link between the Jewish people and our Father in Heaven.

4

My apprenticeship
(CONTINUED)

RABBI KATZENSTEIN is a very engaging American-born, German-Jewish businessman, a member of the Breuer Kehillah (the famous German congregation located in Washington Heights, New York) who has been that community's mohel for the past fifteen years. He is a carefully dressed vibrant young man, obviously a successful businessman, who is in love with his work as a mohel.

Rabbi Katzenstein does not keep a penny of his fees for doing milah; he turns every check over to a worthy charity. This appealed to me a great deal since I could see how refusing personal remuneration allows for more objectivity in the decision-making which often accompanies a mohel's work. For example, in certain circumstances a mohel may be tempted not to delay a bris which truly ought to be postponed because of health considerations beyond the eighth day, for fear of "losing the job" to another mohel; or to do a bris on a child of questionable Jewish ancestry in order to gain a fee.

I took copious notes on everything Rabbi Katzenstein did, even on the way he sharpened his thumbnails. He explained to me that traditional mohalim sharpen both thumbnails to a point because they use these nails after the foreskin is cut away to tear the remaining mucous membrane covering the glans penis. I saw that I would have to let my thumbnails grow a bit before I could file them to a point.

I remember the first bris Rabbi Katzenstein took me to. It was the first-born son of a non-religious Jewish couple who lived in his neighborhood. The apartment was small but lavishly furnished. The guests were slow in arriving, so the bris was delayed about a half hour. During this interval, my teacher showed me how to examine the infant, looking for any change in color and observing various signs of good health. He demonstrated the normal genital anatomy and described the portion which had to be removed, how to grasp the foreskin, and where to apply the *mogen* or shield that guides the knife and protects the penis. He showed me how to probe gently between the *orlah* (foreskin) and the *atorah* (glans penis), to separate these tissues before the bris in order to facilitate the operation.

"There are actually two parts to being a mohel, Reb Chaim," he said to me. "Some excel in one area and are miserable failures in the other. But a good mohel must be expert in both. One aspect of milah is the technical procedure, the surgery. Needless to say, there is no room for anything less than perfection here.

"The second area where excellence is required," he continued, "is in the ritual aspects of the procedure, the performance, so to speak. This takes much practice, but is also vital to the institution of milah. This also includes how you speak to the parents before and after the actual ceremony."

I was soon to see Rabbi Katzenstein in action. The guests had finally arrived. Rabbi Katzenstein swaddled the infant in a tight wrap, immobilizing the child and exposing only the penis. This was the technique which he had learned from the Hungarian mohel who had taught him the craft. The child was then wrapped in a blanket and the ceremony was ready to begin.

Rabbi Katzenstein walked confidently into the living room where the ceremony was to take place, having already arranged his instruments on a small table. He was immaculately dressed; his shoes were highly polished. The dozen or so friends and relatives sensed the beginning of the ceremony and stopped talking. All eyes were on the mohel. I stood quietly behind the *sandek*'s chair so as to get a good view of the mohel's technique.

The mohel nodded to the nurse in the corridor and the baby was brought into the living room. "*Boruch ha-ba,*" he intoned in a strong musical voice, greeting the arrival of the child. Various people handed the baby one to the other as Rabbi Katzenstein conducted the ceremony in Hebrew, occasionally pausing to explain a major point in English. I noticed that this was very much appreciated since most of those present would otherwise have had no understanding of what was going on. Finally, the infant was handed to its father.

Rabbi Katzenstein directed the *sandek*, the one who would hold the baby during the bris, to sit on a specifically designated chair. The father was then instructed to hand his child to the *sandek*, who happened to be one of the infant's grandfathers. Then, without hesitation and quite skillfully, the mohel grasped the foreskin, applied the shield, and said the blessing in Hebrew, "Blessed are You, O Lord our God, Who has made us holy with Your commandments and commanded us concerning circumcision." He reached for his scalpel and deftly amputated the foreskin, quickly split the mucosa with his thumbnails, then applied suction, as is prescribed by Law, using a glass tube which fit around the shaft of the penis. Immediately, he wrapped a narrow gauze bandage around the wound, covered the baby with a blanket and took him from the lap of the *sandek*, whose face by this time was quite pale and covered with a thin sheen of perspiration, and handed him to the other grandfather. This person would hold the baby while he received his Jewish name.

Rabbi Katzenstein filled a silver goblet with a sweet red wine (kosher, of course) and continued the ceremony, first with the blessing "*borey pri hagofen*" on the wine, then with the blessing of the bris itself. He concluded with the naming of the child. In the middle of this last part of the ceremony, he paused to place some wine in the infant's mouth. The baby stopped crying and smacked his lips happily. The nervous tension in the living room was broken and the audience laughed.The child was named and everyone said *mazal tov, mazal tov*—the ancient and holy ceremony of bris milah was completed. Now it was up to the parents to bring up this baby in the ways of his God, in the traditions of his people. Another link in the chain, stretching back to Abraham our Father, had been forged. The Covenant had been sealed in the flesh of a new generation.

Right afterwards, we checked the baby to see if the bleeding was under control. This was a relatively bloody circumcision, Rabbi Katzenstein explained, because of the thickness of the foreskin. But everything was all right and the dressing did not require changing.

Since this bris occurred right in the neighborhood, we were able to return to the parents' home soon after *maariv* (evening services in the synagogue) for another look at the infant. The dressings were soaked with urine but there was no new bleeding. The rabbi pointed out that there was no cause to be concerned about the effects of urine on the raw wound since the urine of a newborn baby is quite dilute and not at all caustic. He instructed the parents that the only bleeding they should call him about would be if blood should be observed dripping down the child's legs. A small amount of seepage through the gauze dressings could be expected and should not be at all worrisome. He assured them that he would return in the morning to remove the long narrow gauze bandage now wrapped around the wound.

The mohel exuded professionalism and obviously generated complete trust and confidence in the parents of the child. I made a note of this.

A pillow that was placed on the sandek's knees, on which the infant was then held. The picture on the ornamented covering represents Elijah and the city of Jerusalem.

5

The mohel's instruments

AN ANCIENT TRADITION

THE BASIC INSTRUMENT used to perform a bris milah is the *izmel* or knife, sometimes referred to in Yiddish as the *mohel-messer* (literally, the mohel's knife). Nowadays, we use a metal blade, though in early Biblical times a sharpened flint instrument would have been used. The Law allows any material to be used except the sharp edge of any substance which might leave splinters in the wound (such as a reed). Although surgical scissors would be allowed, the universal custom has been to use a metal blade.

Most traditional mohalim use a knife forged out of a single piece of surgical steel with a double-edged blade. The instrument is sharpened on both sides to conform with King David's proclamation in the 149th Psalm: "Let the praises of the Lord be in their mouth, and a double-edged sword in their hand. . . ." Some mohalim claim that it is difficult for them to keep such an instrument razor-sharp and have thus taken to using disposable surgical scalpel blades, which are used once and then discarded.

I, myself, have five milah knives, all of the traditional design. The higher-quality instruments are manufactured by David Lublinsky of Tel Aviv, and those of poorer workmanship, though of equal sharpness, are manufactured by a non-Jewish firm in Great Britain. I use the latter instruments when I have to do a circumcision in the operating room, for example on an adult Russian, and have to entrust my instruments to a nurse for autoclaving. So prized are my Israeli knives that I never let them out of my sight.

A good knife is a balanced instrument easily grasped in the operator's hand and whose razor-sharp blade keeps its edge even after repeated use. Before a bris, I sharpen the edges of this instrument on a razor strop and test its acuity on the flesh of the palm of my hand. By feeling the edge in this manner, it is very easy to tell whether a blade is at its sharpest. When

Above: a circumcision knife of steel with an ivory handle, made in Holland in 1716. Below: a modern milah knife of stainless steel, from England.

the blade is brand new, however, it is not very sharp at all and must be brought to a fine edge by one who is highly skilled in such things. A friendly *shochet* (ritual slaughterer) who lives in my neighborhood obliges me in this matter. It is a pleasure to see him work, since he is quite a master craftsman. A *mohel-messer*, with a blade of only two or three inches, is child's play for him. A *shochet*'s knife, though sharpened on only one edge, is 18 or 20 inches in length and must not only be razor-sharp but also *absolutely free* of the slightest nick. This last requirement does not apply to the mohel's knife.

The blade of the mohel's knife is between two and three inches in length. Though I prefer the shorter variety, I have used a three inch blade without difficulty. The problem with the longer blade is that it is a little too long for a tiny infant and there is always a slight danger of nicking the baby's thigh or the *sandek*'s fingers with the far end of the knife. Of course, a longer blade is advantageous when performing a circumcision on an adult since the amount of flesh to cut is so much greater.

Some mohalim allow the father of the child to hold the knife just prior to the milah to signify that the mitzvah or commandment to perform a bris milah on his son is really *his* responsibility and that the mohel is only acting as his *shaliach* or agent. Although I try to remember to tell every father this at the time of the bris and make certain that he understands the fact that he is making me a *shaliach* to do the mitzvah, I allow only certain fathers actually to hold the knife. If

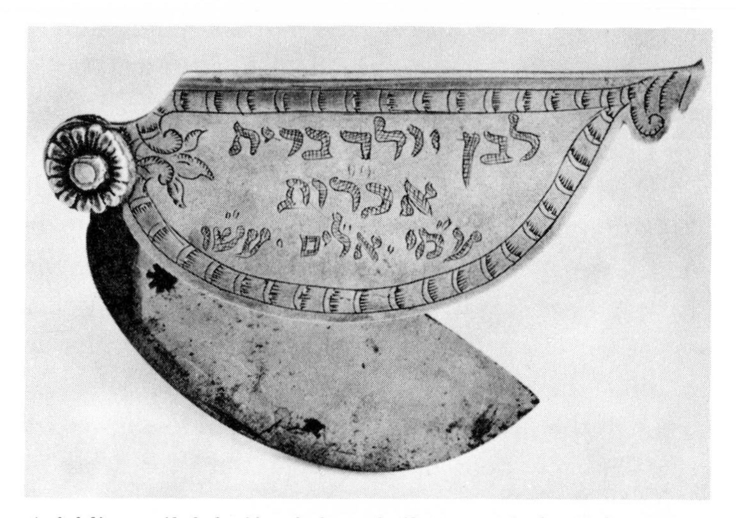

*A folding milah knife of chased silver, made in 19th-century Italy. Inscribed is a Hebrew text meaning "With a newborn son will I [*haShem*] make a covenant"; the last word,* echroth, *may well have been meant to indicate the year of its making: the numerical values of its letters add up to 1897. Below are three abbreviations: The first and third denote the Scriptural verse,* ezri me'im haShem osei shomayim vo'oretz *("My help is from the Lord, maker of heaven and earth"). The middle abbreviation denotes Elchanan Yedidyah Manzi, evidently the name of the child for whose circumcision the knife was made.*

they appear sufficiently composed so that they will not drop the knife as they hand it to me, I will let them hold it before the bris.

There is a custom to leave the knife, suitably wrapped of course, under the pillow of the baby's mother the night before the bris. One mohel, who formerly observed this custom, told me of one father who had asked him to leave the *izmel* he was planning to use at the home. When the mohel replied, "I no longer do this because I have lost too many knives that way," the father answered, "Oh, don't worry. We still have the knife you left for the last baby."

I have not adopted this custom myself.

Having more than one knife is sometimes helpful. For example, if a mohel should have two brissim to do on the same Shabbos, he would be able to leave one complete set of instruments at one house and another set at the other. This would be necessary because on Shabbos he may not carry his instruments outside. Though the performance of a bris itself is allowed on the Shabbos, none of the preparations for a bris—forbidden by various Shabbos laws—are permitted.

I was once asked to perform three brissim on the same day—a case of triplets! I was fortunate to have three high quality blades for that happy occasion. More about this remarkable event later.

Some mohalim use only one piece of equipment — a knife. The entire procedure is otherwise done "free-hand." This takes great skill and, in the hands of an inexperienced operator, would endanger the infant. For the past three or four hundred years, perhaps longer, another instrument has been used in ritual circumcision. This is the guide or shield (*blechel* in Yiddish, *mogen* in Hebrew). Both names are appropriate because it both guides the knife and shields the glans penis from harm.

The shield really looks like a shield. It is a thin strip of silver-plated metal about one inch by two inches with a slit about two-thirds the length of its longer dimension (see illustration). The width of the midline slit is a little more than one millimeter (about the thinness of a dime) though slightly wider in shields used for older children. When the foreskin is drawn forward prior to its amputation by the mohel, the shield is placed over the foreskin between the mohel's fingers and the glans penis in the direction he wishes to cut. The knife is passed across the shield between the shield and the mohel's fingers. The shield thus guides the razor edge of the knife in the proper direction and at the proper angle while at the same time offering complete protection to the child's penis and scrotum.

I have accumulated more than a dozen shields of different sizes, shapes and manufacture. The best shields are not made in Israel but in Great Britain. The British shields are works of art, perfectly balanced, well machined, and ideally shaped. They are of adequate size and weight, whereas the Israeli shields I have are, in my opinion, too thick and heavy, and those of American manufacture are either too

Two modern-day circumcision shields of stainless steel, made in England (photographically reduced). The one with the wider slit is for use with older children.

small to provide adequate protection or of too wide an aperture.

With an infant, an aperture of slightly more than one millimeter is adequate. With an older child up to the age of about ten or twelve, an aperture of 1.75 mm is necessary. Infrequently, an especially small aperture is necessary in certain very tiny infants. I try to be prepared for all possibilities and always take several shields with me to a bris. Although I have usually examined the baby the day before the bris, it is not always possible to estimate the thickness of the foreskin until I actually probe the space between the glans penis and the foreskin just before the ceremony.

This brings me to the next piece of equipment which has traditionally been used by mohalim for at least four hundred years and possibly much longer: the *probe*. This is a thin silver instrument with a smooth blunt end about the thickness of the lead of a wooden lead pencil, perhaps about 6 inches in length. It is used to gently lift the foreskin and its mucous undersurface from the surface of the glans penis. This facilitates the performance of the bris.

A probe (photographically reduced)

Almost all the mohalim with whom I spoke used a probe as a regular part of their procedure. On several occasions, I have performed a bris without first probing to separate the mucosal surface of the foreskin from the glans penis, but experienced much more difficulty with the second part of the bris milah, the *priah* or the splitting and peeling back of this mucosal layer of tissue.

My routine practice is now to probe the infant's foreskin, either a few minutes before the bris, while the baby is still in his nursery or bedroom, or immediately at the beginning of the bris itself as the infant is being held by the *sandek*.

One halachic difficulty with the use of the probe is its use on Shabbos or Yom Tov, since its application to the tender tissue of the infant's genitalia occasionally causes a little bleeding. And drawing blood on Shabbos or Yom Tov, except in the actual performance of the bris itself, is Biblically forbidden. Some mohalim avoid this problem by doing the probing the day before. However, this occasionally causes some swelling and may make more difficult the subsequent milah on the following day. Others simply skip the probing altogether on Shabbos or Yom Tov.

Another school of thought, to which I adhere, holds that if the probing is done immediately before the milah, say, while the infant is on the *sandek*'s knees, it then becomes assimilated into the entire procedure of the bris and is therefore permitted.

6

The mohel's instruments

WHEN NEW IS NOT NECESSARILY BETTER

THUS FAR, I have discussed instruments about the use of which there is little if any controversy. A bris milah performed with only a knife, a shield, and a probe would probably meet with acceptance and approbation in even the most traditional Jewish circles. Now I would like to mention a few instruments which do not find such universal approval.

A great many mohalim grasp the two layers of the foreskin (to review: the outer layer is called in Hebrew the *orlah*, the inner layer the *or hapriah*) with a hemostat, holding them firmly together as they pull the foreskin forward and apply the shield. Thus, when the knife is used, both layers of skin are cut simultaneously (*b'vas achas*), removing completely both the foreskin and the mucous membrane under it. There is in this manner no opportunity or need to perform a *priah* since the *or hapriah* has been completely removed.

Although some well-known mohalim claim that the use of a hemostat (*tzvingle* in Yiddish) has its sources in ancient rabbinic literature, others criticize its use because it eliminates that part of the milah known as the *priah*. They maintain that the separate step of splitting and peeling back the *or hapriah* is desirable and necessary for traditional, halachic, and kabbalistic or mystical reasons. However, no one, to my knowledge, would claim that such a bris was after the fact not completely kosher.

I use the hemostat technique extremely infrequently on infants. I recall one case in which I was asked to do the bris on an infant whose older brother had been circumcised by another mohel. The family was not at all pleased with the appearance of the earlier ritual circumcision. When I examined the older child, who was eight years old, the reason for their dissatisfaction was clear. The child was quite chubby and had a very small penis, though well within the normal range for his age. The combination of these two factors resulted in the child's penis being retracted within the abdominal fat pad, and excess tissue on the shaft of the penis was then pushed over the glans penis giving it the appearace of being uncircumcised.

I advised the parents that this situation would improve somewhat as the child grew older and advanced through puberty. Not only would the size of the penis increase, but the distribution of fat would change, both factors combining to give him a more circumcised appearance.

When I examined the baby brother, I noted that his penis was also quite diminutive, though within the range of normality. I knew that I would have to remove every bit of excess tissue or the result would be less than cosmetic, and possibly a halachic problem. The *or hapriah* would have to be removed completely, and to do this I elected to use a hemostat so as to better grasp the tissue which would be cut away during the bris.

Everything went well and the results were entirely pleasing to both the family and mohel. I checked the child a month after the bris and knew I had taken the right approach. However, I reserve the use of the hemostat, in the case of infants, for such special cases. Although there are no halachic reasons to criticize those mohalim who routinely use the hemostat method, I feel that there is no special advantage to its utilization. I myself find that I can remove the proper amount of foreskin and an adequate portion of the underlying mucous membrane layer without the use of unnecessary instrumentation.

When performing a bris in the operating room, however, I will use the hemostat technique since it is critical to remove tissue in such a way that the surgeon will then be able to oppose the edges of cut skin exactly in order to suture them easily. If he has to trim away excess mucosal membrane, there will usually be a great deal more post-operative swelling because of the extra handling and irritation of these very sensitive tissues. Yet, even in the operating room, I never remove all the *or hapriah* but am careful to leave about a fourth of it in place. This is then pushed back over the shaft of the penis and sutured to the shaft skin with a chromic suture which does not have to be removed but which dissolves by itself.

Another controversial item is the glass tube or barrel sometimes used to perform the third essential stage of the milah, the *metzitzah* or drawing of blood from the wound. (You recall: the first stage of the milah is the removal of the foreskin, the second stage is the splitting of the mucosal membrane.) From earliest times to the present day, this third step has been done by mouth. In some circles a glass device is used, one end of which fits over the end of the penis, the other end of which is tapered and through which the mohel can apply suction. Such a device is used in many modern Orthodox circles and even among the most traditional of the German Jewish communities. In fact, Rabbi Katzenstein told me that at a bris he performed on the grandson of Rabbi Shimon Schwab, one of the leaders of the German Jewish community of Washington Heights (the Breuer Kehillah), he was instructed to use the glass tube in the performance of the *metzitzah* to make it publicly clear that the use of this instrument was indeed equivalent to the ancient practice of *metzitzah b'peh* (literally, withdrawal of the blood by mouth).

The traditional practice of *metzitzah b'peh*, which has its roots in the earliest history of the Jewish people and has survived unchanged to the present time, should be viewed with great respect. It is spoken of very positively in the Jewish literature on circumcision both as an essential part of the ritual and as a health measure which prevents infection and promotes healing. Although there are certain circumstances where a glass tube may be used, most Jewish sages speak strongly in favor of (and some insist on) *metzitzah b'peh* without additional instrumentation.

An instrument which many mohalim retain on a stand-by basis—that is, not used unless necessary—is the *priah* scissors. This is a small but very sharp scissors, the points of which have been blunted and shaped into little knobs so that they can only cut but will not prick. This instrument is used if for one reason or the other the mohel is unable to split the *or hapriah* with his thumbnails. Occasionally, the *or hapriah* is just too thick to tear manually. Sometimes, it is almost impossible to get a firm enough grasp of this slippery tissue to tear it evenly, in which case the mohel may choose to start the process of splitting with a little nick, using the *priah* scissors. I use this

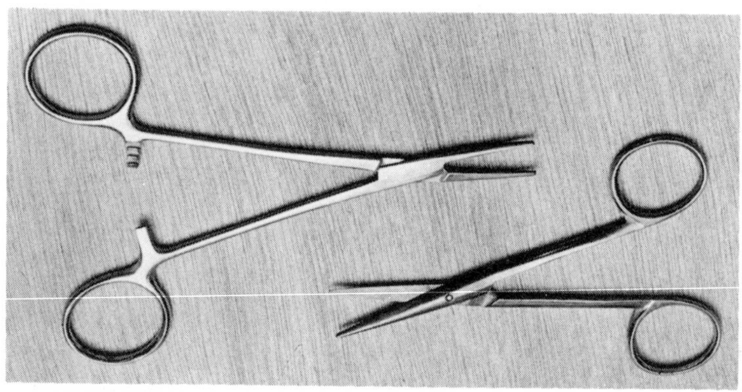

Left: a hemostat occasionally used for priah
Right: a priah scissors (both photographically reduced)

instrument whenever I circumcise an older child, since after infancy this membrane is always thickened and cannot be divided with the thumbnails.

To my knowledge, there are no halachic problems with the occasional use of this instrument.

No discussion of circumcision instruments would be complete without at least passing reference to a modern innovation marketed under the name of the Mogen Circumcision Instrument or the Bronstein Clamp. This item resembles the shield except that it is made of a heavier construction and is hinged above the aperture which fits over the foreskin. It is always used in conjunction with the hemostat so that both layers of foreskin tissue are removed simultaneously. After the foreskin has been probed and drawn forward with the hemostat, the Bronstein Clamp is placed over it. It is oriented in the same manner as the shield which has been discussed previously. It is then clamped shut, simultaneously crimping and devitalizing the tissue of the foreskin in its steel jaws. Hemostasis is also achieved through this crushing pressure of its blades and indeed, when it is removed, there may be no bleeding at all from the skin edges of the circumcision wound.

There are two halachic objections to the use of this instrument. First, bris milah requires the removal of living tissue! Using this clamp, the mohel will be cutting across already devitalized or non-living tissue and there is then a question whether or not his blessing, "*al ha-milah,*" is a *brocho le-vatoloh* (a blessing said in vain). The second and major objection is that this technique may be completely bloodless. *Dam bris* (blood of the Covenant) is an essential aspect of the milah. Indeed, all would agree that if such a tool were used and there was no blood whatsoever issuing from the surface of the circumcision wound, a ritual drawing of blood (*hatofas dam bris*) should be done at a later date.

Most *poskim* (learned rabbis who decide on matters of Jewish law) do not approve of the Mogen Clamp or any type of clamping device. Indeed, this instrument has been forbidden by the *Agudas Horabonim*, whose president at the time of writing is Rabbi Moshe Feinstein.

Because of the many halachic problems and the lack of a *mesorah* (tradition) for the use of the Mogen Clamp, I would suggest that it be used *only* in very special cases (for example, if the only mohel available is not trained in the traditional methods of milah) and then *only after prior consultation with a competent Orthodox rabbi*, who must give his permission for the exceptional use of this device. If this instrument must be employed, the mohel should be asked to use it in such a way that there will be some bleeding after the bris. This can be achieved by applying the Mogen immediately before the milah and removing it right after the foreskin has been removed. If no blood flows, a gentle massage of the cut edges of the milah wound will usually result in a small amount of bleeding.

Mention should be made of some of the surgical instruments such as the Gomco Clamp, the Plastibell, and other such devices used by obstetricians and pediatricians today. Not only are these instruments somewhat dangerous and unnecessarily painful for the infant; they are halachically inadvisable. Some religious authorities hold that a child circumcised with such a device may require *hatofas dam bris,* the ritual compensatory drawing of a drop of blood from the site of the circumcision. Only in such a way would the milah be completely acceptable to all authorities.

Indeed, a number of young men have been sent to me for just such a procedure. These are usually boys from non-Orthodox backgrounds who have become observant Jews and want to be sure that their bris milah is one hundred percent kosher. The blood is drawn from the edge of the glans with a tiny prick of a very sharp needle. There is almost no pain and only a drop or two of blood is lost. No *brocho* is made since there is only a suspicion or doubt concerning the validity of the previous bris. (The general principle is that when there is a doubt over the necessity of making a blessing, the blessing is not made.)

I have seen one mohel in a New York hospital use a scissors when doing ritual circumcisions on older children (Russians) under general anesthesia. The use of scissors is permitted and specifically mentioned in the *Shulchan Aruch*, the Code of Jewish Law, which the entire observant Jewish world follows.

There is some controversy, however, about the use of anesthetics during a bris. Certainly it is *never* used on an infant, nor is there any justification whatsoever for its use in such a case. Anyone observing a ritual circumcision skillfully done on an eight day old child cannot fail to observe how little pain the infant must endure. The child cries more when he is being held, not when the foreskin is being incised. As soon as the infant's legs are released and a drop of wine or milk touches his lips, the crying usually stops. The infant is frequently cranky the first night after the bris, but probably from the irritation of the bandaging rather than from pain.

It has been my experience that the procedure is generally painless up to at least four or five months of age. In older children, adequate local anesthesia is achieved by injecting a little Xylocaine at the base of the penis. This has proved a satisfactory method even in adults.

Many older children and adults, however, prefer to have the procedure done under general anesthesia. Indeed, many would defer the operation indefinitely if this option were not available to them. The *halachah* discusses all three possibilities in the ritual circumcision of adult Jewish males—without anesthesia, with local anesthesia only, and with general anesthesia. Since a substantial body of halachic opinion permits the use of general anesthesia, I have not hesitated to allow this option to any uncircumcised Jewish male who is to undergo a ritual circumcision.

Procedure in the operating room is of necessity somewhat different than it is in the privacy of my own office or of the patient's home. In the operating room, the young man receives his initiation into the Covenant of Abraham while in deep sleep. The genitalia have been thoroughly cleansed with Betadine solution. He is then draped in sterile sheets, only the penis being exposed through a small window in the dressings. I make the *brocho* after covering the genitalia since it is not halachically appropriate to say a *brocho* in the presence of the exposed private parts of an adult or even an older child. I then perform the milah in the usual way using a shield and the traditional double-edged knife. The *priah* may be accomplished with a *priah* scissors since the mucous membrane under the foreskin is too thick in the older child or adult to be torn with the thumbnails. *Metzitzah* is accomplished with the barrel of a large hypodermic syringe. The ritual is now over and the attending urologist sews up the skin edges. I make the blessings over the goblet of wine and name the child (adult) right there in the operating room or in the recovery room right after surgery.

When a bris on an adult is done in the home, there is no suturing. Hemostasis (stopping the bleeding) and proper alignment of the skin edges are achieved by wrapping the wound area with a 12″ x 1″ sterile gauze dressing. The wound heals completely in eight or nine days. When sutures are used, the healing process is somewhat longer.

7

The Rebbe's Einickle

FROM RUSSIA WITH LOVE

I REMEMBER the first ritual circumcision I ever performed. It was on a sixteen-year-old boy. This was not the first time I had ever done a circumcision, since I had performed this surgery a number of times while a medical student. Nor was it, accurately speaking, the first time I had performed ritual milah, as I had been called several times by the funeral chapel to circumcise deceased infants. (More later about the circumcision of stillborn infants and deceased neonates.)

This particular bris was especially meaningful to me not only because it was to be my first ritual circumcision on a living subject but also because the boy, a recent arrival from the Soviet Union, was a descendant of the *Alter Rebbe*, Rabbi Shneur Zalman of Liadi, the originator of Chabad *chassidus* and founder of the Lubavitch dynasty. And it had been the seventh leader of Lubavitch, Rabbi Menachem

Mendel Schneerson, the present Lubavitcher Rebbe, who only a few months before had given me his permission, encouragement, and blessing to become a mohel.

The story of the remarkable exodus of Jews from the Soviet Union has yet to be told. I suspect that many details will remain undisclosed for many years. Why, after maintaining an iron curtain around itself for almost 60 years, has the Soviet Union decided to allow its Jewish population the possibility of emigration, a possibility enjoyed by no other Soviet minority? Were the Jewish people so totally indigestible in the stomach of the Russian bear that after a half century of trying to assimilate this unpleasant meal into his system, he finally vomited up this stiff-necked people? Or were there other factors involved? I can only guess.

Whatever the reasons were, the city of Cleveland found itself with ever-increasing numbers of new Russian Jewish arrivals. Most of the boys and young men were, as I mentioned in Chapter One, uncircumcised, since this operation is not allowed in the Soviet Union except for strict medical indications. What were we to do?

Since my return from New York, I had been spending a great deal of time with Rabbi Shlomo Davis, the well-known and very expert mohel of the Telshe Yeshiva, which is located just a few miles from Cleveland. I tried to be present at every bris he performed and spent many hours discussing the various intricacies of the operation and the ritual. He was extremely helpful and cooperative, and much of the skill I presently possess I directly relate to his training. But I had no exposure to the modified procedures required in the performance of bris milah on an adult.

Rebbetzin Zalman Kazen came to the rescue. She is an indefatigable worker on behalf of these newly arrived Russian Jewish immigrants and toils day and night to re-introduce them to the traditions of their grandparents, all but forgotten after two generations of life in a repressive socialist society. Together, she and I launched the "Russian Project" under the auspices of the *Neshei Chabad* organization in Cleveland, although she did and continues to do most of the work. As soon as a family arrives in Cleveland, Mrs. Kazen is on the spot with *mezuzos* for their new apartment, books in Russian about *kashrus* and the Jewish holidays, and "Shabbos kits" consisting of a bottle of wine, a goblet, candlesticks, a *challah* knife, spice box, and a Russian-Hebrew *siddur*.

Having grown up in Russia herself, Mrs. Kazen not only speaks a fluent Russian and Yiddish but completely understands the psyche of these new immigrants. She knows what they've been through and has a gut-feeling for their needs. Her approach has produced miracles. Homes which have been completely devoid of Jewish content for half a century now boast some observance of Shabbos. Doorposts bear *mezuzos*. Approximately one hundred Russian children are enrolled in the Hebrew Academy, Cleveland's Orthodox Jewish day school. And almost one hundred and fifty boys and young men have been ritually circumcised.

This last accomplishment was no easy task. Before I learned how to do milah, it was necessary to send boys to New York. Needless to say, this was a very expensive undertaking since it involved not only flying the youngster to New York but also his mother, to say nothing of the medical expenses once they got there. Toward the end of June, Mrs. Kazen had rounded up five boys, ranging in age from three to eighteen years and had arranged to fly in a mohel from New York who was well known for his skill and experience in doing adult ritual circumcision.

The occasion of these ritual circumcisions was my first meeting with Rabbi Eliyahu Shain, a young man who lives in the Crown Heights section of Brooklyn, the neighborhood of the Lubavitcher Chassidim. I was quite surprised to learn that although he did a great many brissim in the Lubavitch community, he himself was not a Lubavitcher. He had received his training in milah, both for infants and adults, in Israel, and was now the proprietor of a small bookstore in Brooklyn. He was also a skilled *sofer* (scribe), and sold and repaired *tefillin*, *mezuzos*, and other religious items in his store in addition to *s'forim* (Jewish books).

He was very likable and we hit it off well from the start. We agreed that he would show me how to perform milah on these young people. He would do the first two brissim and I would watch. I would do the next three under his close supervision.

The instruments he brought with him were the *izmel*, or mohel's knife, a probe, a shield, and *priah* scissors. In addition, he brought a bottle of antiseptic, with which he sterilized his instruments, and a considerable amount of gauze bandage to dress the wounds after the milah.

I asked him what kind of anesthesia he utilized, and was quite surprised to hear that he did not use any at all. At one time, he told me, he injected a local anesthetic at the site of the milah, into the foreskin itself, but he felt that this procedure distorted the landmarks he used for making the incision and he discontinued this practice. The idea of operating on a grown person without the benefit of anesthesia was hard for me to share. I felt that I could achieve adequate anesthesia without distorting the field of surgery, so I brought along some hypodermic syringes and several bottles of 1% Xylocaine (without epinephrine). I knew of a technique whereby the anesthetic is injected under the skin at the base of the penis, far away from the foreskin, which results in adequate anesthesia lasting for at least twenty minutes, more than enough time to perform the entire operation, including bandaging. Yet, I wanted to see his technique.

The first candidate was a nervous teenager who appeared quite anxious about the whole business—anxious to begin and get it over with, and anxious to enter the Covenant of Abraham. Rabbi Shain first asked him to shave the pubic area—primarily to avoid having strands of hair catch in the wound or in the bandaging and cause pain during the initial healing process. After the shaving, the genitalia were cleansed. Rabbi Shain then probed under the foreskin to free any adhesions between it and the glans penis, though such adhesions are somewhat unlikely in a boy of this age. We were now ready to start the bris milah.

The mohel covered the boy's genitalia and said the *brocho*, "Blessed art Thou, O Lord our God, King of the Universe, Who has sanctified us with His commandments and commanded us concerning milah." It was necessary to cover the genitalia since it is not permitted to say any *brocho* or mention God's name in the presence of *ervah*, a Hebrew term including male genitalia or any parts of the female that are usually covered.

He then quickly grasped the foreskin with the first two fingers and thumb of his left hand and pulled the foreskin forward, slipping on the large silver shield with his right hand. He had previously lubricated the aperture of this shield so that it would slip on easily over the thick *orlah*. At this point, the boy cried out since this device pinches the foreskin and is painful. Without a moment's hesitation, Rabbi Shain took his knife, the traditional two-edged *izmel*, and passed it along the shield between the shield and his fingers, removing the foreskin in one rapid motion. The shield was not quite long enough to include the entire foreskin so that the last half inch of it was removed "free-hand," that is, without the guidance of the shield. Rabbi Shain was careful not to remove too much skin from the undersurface of the penis.

The next step involved inserting a blade of the *priah* scissors under the mucous membrane which lies just under the foreskin, dividing it in the midline up to and over the ridge of the glans penis. The split membrane was then pushed up over the shaft of the penis.

After this thin membrane was split, the tissues were held in place with a long gauze wrapping one inch wide and perhaps a foot in length. In addition to holding the freshly cut edges in place, it also served to stop the bleeding. The bandaging took only half a minute.

It was all over. Any pain had subsided. A mitzvah had been accomplished. The Russian smiled weakly. He now bore the holy sign of the covenant which God struck between Himself and Abraham four thousand years ago and which He established as an eternal compact between Him and His chosen people from then until eternity.

I was very moved by the significance of what I had just seen, but wondered if all the pain was necessary. Perhaps, if adequate local anesthesia could have been achieved, there would not have been the pressure to work so quickly. These same thoughts occurred to me during the circumcision of this boy's younger brother, who was only eight years old. He was very frightened and struggled during the whole procedure, especially when the pain began with the application of the shield.

Rabbi Shain gave the boys' parents some instructions concerning aftercare and told them that he would return the next morning to remove the dressings. We left to see our next young Russian. This was going to be my turn...my first bris.

"I wonder, Rabbi Shain," I asked after we arrived at the next boy's home, "if you would have any objections to my using a little local anesthesia? I'll show you how to use it without tissue swelling getting in the way of the surgery."

He seemed interested and readily agreed.

Our next subject was 16 years old. He, along with his mother and stepfather, had arrived from Italy only a few weeks earlier, and was determined to be circumcised. When he told me his grandmother was a Schneerson and a descendant of the *Alter Rebbe*, I knew it was no coincidence that I had been given such strong encouragement by the Rebbe to take up the practice of milah.

He had already shaved and cleansed the pubic area and was lying on his bed. We placed a number of towels under him to protect the sheets and mattress from the bleeding.

"You see," I said to Rabbi Shain, "I am going to achieve anesthesia by injecting Xylocaine at the base of the penis, just under the skin, where the nerves which supply the foreskin are located as they travel to the end of the penis."

I filled a 10 cc disposable syringe with 6 cc of 1% Xylocaine (without epinephrine) and, after wiping the skin with an alcohol pledget, gently made the injection at the circumference of the base of the penis, close to the abdominal wall. The boy winced. Within ten minutes, the medicine had taken effect: the skin of the penis was insensitive to pain. I pinched the foreskin with my fingernails, and he felt nothing. I was ready to begin.

Slowly and for the first time in my life, I said the *brocho*, "Blessed art Thou . . . Who has commanded us concerning milah." I uncovered the genitalia, firmly grasped the foreskin as Rabbi Shain had showed me, and pulled it forward. Estimating how much skin I wanted to remove, I placed on the shield at that point. At first, I tried amputating the foreskin with the surgical scalpel I had brought with me, but it would not cut the thick flesh of this adolescent prepuce. Evidently, the *Alter Rebbe*'s *einickle* (grandson) was not going to be entered into the Covenant of Abraham with a disposable surgical blade!

Rabbi Shain handed me his *izmel* and I pulled it across the foreskin firmly but with several back-and-forth strokes. The skin was off. The shield fell off, revealing the *atorah* covered with a translucent membrane, the *or hapriah*. There had been no pain.

I took the *priah* scissors and cut the mucous membrane in the midline back to just behind the rim of the *atorah*, pulling it back over the shaft of the penis. *Metzitzah b'peh* completed the bris.

Under Rabbi Shain's watchful eye, I carefully wrapped a snug gauze dressing around the wound, firmly holding the tissues in place and stopping the bleeding. It was done. The boy smiled and said, "Thank you"—one of his few English words.

I was elated. Everything had gone just perfectly. I had done my first bris. No longer was I just *learning* milah. Now I was an actual mohel. I washed my hands and filled the silver goblet with wine (both kindly provided by Mrs. Kazen) to recite the blessings which follow a bris. I noted that my hands were *now* shaking! But I mustered a firm voice, said the blessings, and gave the *Alter Rebbe*'s *einickle* his Jewish name.

Scriptural passages about circumcision and chapters of t'hillim *(Psalms) to be recited for mother and child, written in charming geometric patterns: From a mohel's book (manuscript) in the Ets Haim Library of Amsterdam, written in Leeuwarden, Holland, in 1829.*

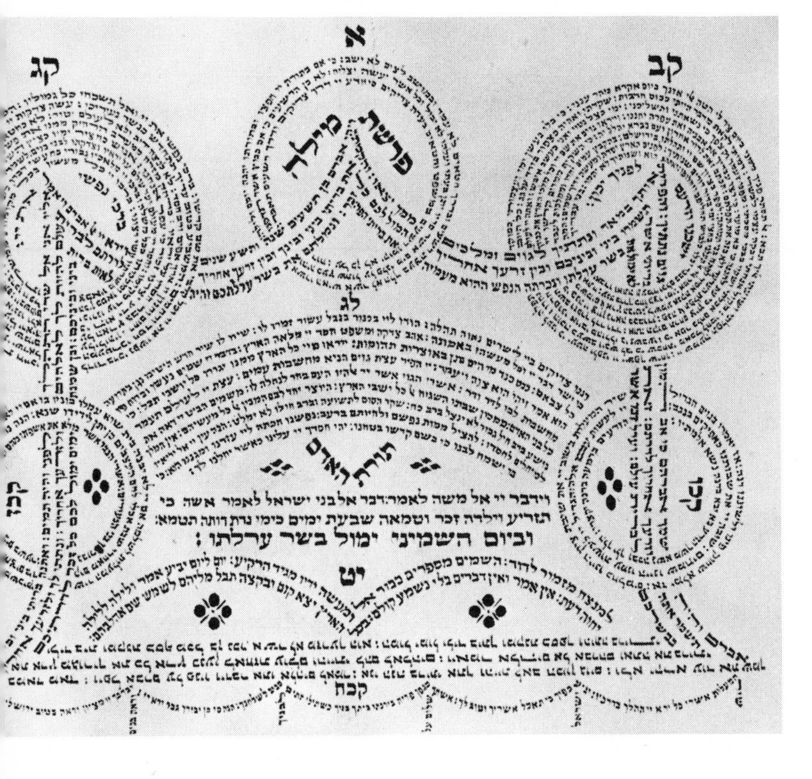

8

On stage: a new mohel in town

THERE WERE A NUMBER OF RUSSIANS who had to have a bris in the few weeks following this first Russian bris, and I rapidly became proficient in doing this type of work, which required a maximum of technical expertise and a minimum of ritual performance. This latter aspect of doing a bris, which Rabbi Katzenstein had referred to—the public performance, the details of the ritual, the ceremony—was still something with which I had little experience. But the opportunity was not long in coming.

Word was getting around the community that there was a new mohel in town, and soon I was asked to perform a bris on an eight-day-old infant.

The family of this child was Orthodox, and the bris would take place in the synagogue. A bris in a synagogue is always a little more difficult for the mohel, because certain conveniences are not available. For example, there is no nearby kitchen sink or soap and hot water. There is usually not even a small wastebasket, or even chairs appropriate to use during the ceremony. There is also often no good place to examine the baby before or after the bris, and the room temperature is usually about ten degrees cooler that in a private home.

I mention these matters in the hope that somewhere, someone with some authority in his synagogue might remedy these matters for his congregation. There are only a few synagogues in Cleveland which have all the above conveniences, and it makes everything much easier for both mohel and infant.

This bris was going to be in a small *shul*, Congregation Tzemach Tzedek, which had none of the preferred conveniences. I knew that an extremely observant and well-informed group of people would attend this bris and I was, understandably, a little nervous. Not only was this going to be my first infant bris, but there would also be no room for error in any aspect of the ceremony. I felt confident about the technical aspects of the surgery, yet knew I was not quite so practiced in the ceremonial aspects.

So, I rehearsed and rehearsed until I knew the blessings almost by heart. I even practiced wearing the *tallis* (prayer shawl), tying the front two *tzitzis* (fringes) together behind me, as I had seen Rabbi Davis do, to prevent them from getting in my way during the bris. I mentally rehearsed every aspect of the ceremony, from the welcoming of the baby into the room to the special blessings and the additions made in the *birkas hamazon* (grace after meals) which would follow the *se'udah* (festive meal) prepared for the bris.

My wife noticed my nervousness, and she put up with a very tense husband that week. She was in fact quite encouraging, pointing out to me that this was certainly not my first bris and that I was not really a newcomer to the ceremonial aspects of a bris, as I had accompanied Rabbi Davis on numerous occasions and had taken copious notes. She was right, of course, but it was not until several years had passed that I did not experience a certain element of stage fright before performing a bris.

Finally, the day arrived. I awoke an hour earlier than usual and reviewed the entire ceremony once again. I drove to the community *mikvah*, arriving about six o'clock. The sun had just risen and a chill was still in the air, even though it was midsummer.

The *mikvah* was freezing. Nonetheless, I undressed and plunged in, whispering a prayer for success in the work ahead of me: "May I be worthy to perform this great mitzvah, equivalent in many respects to the bringing of a *korbon* (sacrifice) on the *mizbeiach* (altar) of the *Beis Hamikdosh* (Holy Temple)."

After the *mikvah*, I attended the *shi'ur* (lesson) in *Gemara*, in which ten or twelve of us in the community participate every morning from 6:30 to 7:30; but my mind was not fully on the discussion at hand. I could think only of the bris. I was very tense.

On the way to the Tzemach Tzedek *shul*, I stopped by the house of the celebrants to examine the child again. He was just fine. I probed gently under the prepuce to loosen the skin a little from the surface of the glans. I gave the mother final instructions about when to arrive with the baby at the *shul*, how to dress the infant, and when to feed him.

The *shul* was packed. In my mind went the thought: they are all here to see my opening performance as the new Cleveland mohel. But in reality, they were there to participate in the *simchah* (festivity) of the bris. Many of my friends were there. Rabbi Bercovic was there, an elderly and saintly man who had arrived in Cleveland a number of years before from the Soviet Union. He had been a very active mohel in Russia, having performed there almost two thousand brissim under the most trying of circumstances. Someone once asked him how he managed to perform the bris in Russia. He looked furtively over his shoulder and whispered, "*B'tzinah!*" (In secret!)

It was very comforting to have another mohel there with me. Indeed, Jewish tradition advises that, if possible, it is well to have at least two mohalim attending each bris. This is for several reasons: first, the other mohel can be consulted if there are any questions concerning an abnormality of the child's genitalia or general physical condition. Two heads are better than one. Second, when there is another mohel present, the mohel performing the bris is less likely to take shortcuts or in any way to abbreviate the ritual, such as omitting *metzitzah b'peh*.

Also present was my faithful companion, Rabbi

בס"ד יום ה' לס' ושמרתם את משמרת הקודש, שנת תשל"ו לפ"ק

השירה הזאת תהי' לעדה

ביד מוכ"ז הרופא ר' **חיים צבי ראמבערג** נ"י

שהוא איש חמודות ומוכתר במעלות ומדות טובות ויראת ה' טהרה הנה
כבר איתמחי גברא אצל גדולי המוהלים ואינו צריך להסכמתי אבל
משום כבודו הנעלה נעניתי לבקשתו והריני מעיד בעדות גמורה
שתהיתי על קנקנו וראיתי בו שהוא אומן גדול ומוחזק במלאכתו
בין מצד הרפואה שזה מעיקר היסודות כדאיתא בשל"ה הקדוש
ובספר אות חיים ושלום, ובין מצד המסורה והרי הוא מובהק
כאחד מזקני המוהלים בכל חלקי המצוה וחזקה על מומחה
כמותו שלא תצא תקלה מתחת ידו ואשרי חלקו שבדור הפרוץ
הזה גברא כמותו קבל על עצמו להכניס בני ישראל בבריתו
של אברהם אבינו יהא רעוא שיזכה לקדש שם שמים וישלם לו
הקב"ה משכורתו הכפולה

בעה"ח לכבוד התורה ושמרי' **שמעון דוד בערקאוויטש**
מוהל מו"ק

באתי בזה להעיד להאי גברא הירא וחרד לדבר ה'
ר' חיים צבי ראמבערג נ"י שהוא מומחה
ומהיר במלאכתו בין בחלק ההלכה ובין בחלק
הרפואה וכמוהו מוהלים המחזיקים במסורת
אבותינו הקדושים ירבו בישראל ובטוחני שלא
יוציא מתחת ידו דבר שאינו מתוקן יהי רצון שיזכה
להכניס ילדי בני ישראל בבריתו של אברהם אבינו

יצחק יהוד' בן הרה"ג הרב עמרם זצ"ל בלום
אב"ד קהל יראים בית עמרם

A certificate issued by Rabbi Simon Berkovic, a mohel who performed circumcisions clandestinely in the Soviet Union till his migration to Cleveland. It attests to the author's ability and authority to perform ritual circumcision. Below it is the attestation of Rabbi Yehuda Blum of Cleveland's Congregation K'hal Yereim.

Moshe Reuven Barkin, who had originally urged me to study milah. I think he took great pride in me.

As soon as the morning *davening* (prayer) was completed, I set up my instruments on a chair at the front of the *shul*. I had brought with me a small paper bag to dispose of waste material, gauze wrappings, and so forth. Since there was no adequate waste container in the *shul*, this was a very useful item to have in my kit; and since then I have always tried to remember to bring a small paper bag to every bris (it has proved useful even in private homes).

I set up several chairs next to my instruments. One chair would be designated the *kisei shel Eliyahu* (Chair of Elijah). The other would be the chair on which the *sandek* would sit as he held the baby during the actual circumcision.

I remember that bris very clearly. I was gratified to hear the words of the preliminary blessings trip so easily and comfortably from my tongue, as if I had been saying them for years. The baby was brought in, first placed on the *kisei shel Eliyahu*, then handed to the father (who was much more nervous than I), and he in turn handed him to the *sandek*, who was the baby's grandfather. The bris itself went without a hitch. Rabbi Berkovic stood behind the *sandek*, keeping a watchful eye on everything and occasionally offering a suggestion in Yiddish.

There was very little bleeding, though the infant chose to urinate during the bris, striking me directly in the eyeglasses. With the confidence of a practiced surgeon, I nonchalantly accepted this passing inconvenience, and finished the bandaging. Everything went well. My underclothes were soaking with sweat, although I kept an outward appearance of calm. I smiled and gave and received *mazal tov*s from one and all. I was physically and emotionally exhausted, but had survived my debut. There was a new mohel in town!

9

Life in America

MY YEARS AS A MOHEL have certainly added a good deal more variety to my daily experience than the routine of a busy physician alone might have, though certainly life as a physician has not been uninteresting. Perhaps it is because I have been practicing medicine so long that the daily excitement of the profession sometimes seems routine, although, to the average non-physician my work might indeed appear glamorous. Witness the proliferation of television programs, movies, and novels which dwell on the work and adventures of aggressive young doctors. To many people, I suppose, a routine sigmoidoscopy or splinter extraction would seem exciting.

But milah remains an exhilarating experience for me. Not only is the procedure wholly a mitzvah, but it is such a prime mitzvah in Jewish life! Moreover, it is a mitzvah which is so rarely done properly that whenever it is performed according to *halachah* I have the feeling that a great impression is being made in worlds unseen, to say nothing of the influence this commandment, "sealed in the flesh," makes upon the young child.

Although it is a surgical procedure, it is unlike any other surgery. And the surroundings in which it is done are so little like the background of most operations. There are no nurses, no scrub-suits, no anesthetics. The setting is usually in the parents' home or their synagogue. Very infrequently, it is the "Ritual Room" (what a horrid name!) of the hospital where the baby is born.

Instead of being surrounded by a host of nurses, aides, and other hospital personnel, the mohel and his young charge are enclosed in the loving atmosphere of a happy family—parents, grandparents, friends, and relatives, all overjoyed to be taking part in this cardinal mitzvah.

Our sages tell us that the mitzvos for which the Jewish people have, in times past, given their lives—such as circumcision—they cling to most tenaciously. This is seen throughout the ages, and even more clearly today, when a great majority of the Jewish people have become careless or forgetful about *kashrus* or Shabbos. This same type of Jew, nevertheless, insists on circumcision for his male offspring. The very thought of an uncircumcised Jewish male raises eyebrows today, even among the most assimilated of our people.

Some homes into which I have been invited to

perform a bris have been very deficient in Jewish knowledge, and I have to explain the most fundamental aspects of Jewish practice to them. The father will have to learn his *brocho* in transliterated Hebrew, since he cannot even read Hebrew letters. The parents will have to call their parents and perhaps grandparents to find out what their own Hebrew names are. I have to explain to the parents that only Jewish people may take part in the bris milah ceremony.

Occasionally, a family gets more than it has bargained for. In one instance, a very assimilated father and mother were adamant that a rabbi or some other religious functionary was *not* to perform the circumcision of their son. Indeed, they were persuaded by a close friend only with the greatest difficulty not to have the circumcision done by their pediatrician in the hospital before the eighth day. Someone told them that there was a doctor in the city who would perform a traditional circumcision in their own home. This suited them just fine.

I, of course, performed a very traditional bris milah, clad as usual in my large flowing *tallis*, and explaining in detail each phase of the ritual. Everyone was interested — no, fascinated! This was so far from their everyday experience. At the end, some of the guests were even moved to don *tefillin* for the first time in their lives. (I always bring a pair of *tefillin* along to a bris, since wearing a pair of kosher *tefillin* at least once during a Jewish man's life has a crucial bearing on his ultimate status in the world to come.)

The parents, grandparents, relatives, and guests were treated to an experience in basic Judaism unlike anything they had ever before seen.

A few months later I received a follow-up message from a distant relative, an Orthodox Jew. He told me that he had been overjoyed to hear that this infant had had a kosher bris milah, but he had complained to the father about not having been invited. After all, of the entire family, he was the one who would have been most anxious to be present at a traditional bris. The father told him with a smile on his lips and a twinkle in his eye, "We didn't know it was going to be a religious affair!"

Evidently I had left a good impression. And I hope that this great mitzvah will lead to many more on the part of this family so distantly removed from their Jewish roots.

I remember another bris in the house of a gentile whose wife was Jewish. A Conservative rabbi had requested that I do this bris, but he asked that I not do the *metzitzah*, since he was concerned about its probable negative effect on a non-religious family. I refused to consent, saying that *metzitzah* was an essential part of the milah and that if there was to be no *metzitzah* I would not do the bris. However, I would take into account the sensibilities of an unlearned and uncommitted American Jewish (and in this case, non-Jewish) public and do the *metzitzah* using the glass tube especially manufactured for the purpose. He reluctantly agreed, still fearing the objections of the family.

However, the objections never materialized and the bris went smoothly. I was a little uncomfortable, since this was the first bris I had ever performed where half the people in attendance were not Jewish. However, the Conservative rabbi seemed quite at ease and impressed one and all—except me. Being more traditional, I could not agree with many of the points he made during his speech, but, out of common courtesy, did not interrupt or correct him.

I recall one bris which was held in a traditional though not Orthodox home. The house was a mansion, and I intended, as is my custom, to do the bris in the living or dining room, wherever the lighting would be better. But the lady of the house, the grandmother, a matronly European, would not have such a "messy and bloody operation" done in her beautiful living room. I insisted, however, saying that a bris is always done in the midst of a "congregation" (a large or sizeable gathering). We compromised. I did the bris in the upstairs nursery and had as many men accompany me as would fit into that small room. The custom is to have at least a *minyan*, ten Jewish males, present and I had more than that. Afterwards, we all marched downstairs and named the child in the expensively appointed living room, surrounded by oil paintings, period furniture, and tapestries.

Other homes were so threadbare that Chabad House (the Lubavitch community center) had to provide the very food for the *se'udah* following the bris. And, yet, these were some of the most joyous brissim at which I have ever been honored to officiate.

I remember one Russian home where there was not even a piece of furniture strong enough to support the weight of the *sandek*, and I had to bring my wife's kitchen step-chair. (Indeed, it proved to be such a good item at a bris that now I often bring it along if the host family does not have a chair high enough for me.) The baby's grandmother had just been admitted to a local hospital suffering from a stroke and the family was, to say the least, in a disorganized state.

In we marched, Mrs. Kazen and I. She not only spoke fluent Russian, but was also totally understanding of their problems, and had the situation in hand in a few minutes. The tables were set with food and with the paper and plastic dinnerware she brought. Her husband, Rabbi Zalman Kazen, and I saw to it that all the adult males among the relatives donned *tallis* and *tefillin* before the ceremony commenced. Every step of the bris milah ritual was explained in Russian to all present.

It was truly a beautiful affair. Hardly a few weeks in this country, this family had been introduced to a genuine Jewish celebration, truly a *Yiddishe simchah*.

I am often amazed by such comments as "My, you work so fast"; or "I don't think I've ever seen a bris done as quickly as you just did." Such remarks, which I hear surprisingly often, never cease to cause me wonder because in my own estimation I do not work fast at all. Indeed, I have never aspired to be the fastest mohel in town. I believe that it is far more important to be careful and deliberate in any medical or surgical procedure, and especially in milah.

Yet I wonder whom my audience is comparing me with when they compliment me on my speed . . . certainly not other mohalim who work in the Cleveland area, since I am no faster than they. However, when compared to the very cumbersome, painful, and complicated techniques used in hospitals (such as with the Plastibell or the Gomco Clamp), the *ritual method* is much more rapid. The actual surgical part of the bris milah in the hands of the competent mohel need not take longer than five or ten seconds, and if we include positioning the infant on the lap of the *sandek* as well as applying the dressing on the wound after the circumcision, the total time is still only about a minute.

I believe that people who are enjoying themselves in a *Yiddishe simchah*, a happy occasion of profound Jewish content, do not notice the passage of time. Just as time speeds by for a person who enjoys *davening* with a Shabbos *minyan* in *shul*, so do hours seem as minutes and minutes as seconds when any Jew is involved wholeheartedly in a Jewish precept, a mitzvah. I try my utmost to make a ritual circumcision just such a happy and meaningful occasion to all present. Actually, the brissim I perform may even take a little longer than is standard because I take great pains to explain every aspect of the ceremony to the family and guests. There is such a vast ignorance of even the most elementary Jewish matters that I could actually talk for hours; I have to stop myself from prolonging my explanations too much. After all, it is better to leave people interested in hearing more from you than to leave them bored and glad you have stopped talking.

In this sterile antiseptic age when the American public eschews exposure to anything remotely unpleasant (witness the American-style funeral or the many euphemisms for death and disease), it is quite surprising to find that everyone at a bris is grateful when you allow them to see exactly what is going on. Some mohalim huddle over their work so that no one can see what they are doing. I think that this overconcern with the supposed sensitivities of family and friends is inappropriate and misguided. Let the people see exactly what a ritual circumcision is. Let them view the "before and after" appearance. They will then have a much greater appreciation for this symbol of the eternal covenant between the Jewish nation and the Creator.

10

Advice to parents

PREPARING FOR A BRIS

FIRST THINGS FIRST: Call the mohel and introduce yourself. But how does one choose a mohel?

By now certain qualities and qualifications will probably seem obvious to you. Certain minimum standards must be met:

1. The mohel must be technically competent to perform the surgery. This is of course a *sine qua non* and cannot be compensated for by any other qualities. No matter how great a reputation for honesty and piety, for learning and Torah knowledge, technical competence remains primary. Many times a mohel of advanced age is as adept as a younger man, but often this is not the case. One must never let the fear of hurting a man's feelings prevent him from choosing a mohel of steady hands, keen mind, and consumate skill.

2. The mohel must be God-fearing. He must be one who plies his trade for the sake of the great, precious mitzvah which he is privileged to perform. He must take his Judaism seriously. If the mohel shaves with a razor blade, drives on Shabbos, or eats in non-kosher restaurants, *he is not fit for the office of mohel and should not be used.* Indeed, a milah he performs might be considered in the eyes of the Law no bris at all. Do not take chances.

3. I would add a third quality: that of *mentshlichkeit.* Will the mohel be able to relate to you and your family and guests? Will he be willing to extend himself to advise you whom to honor at the bris and how to arrange the *se'udah* afterward? Do you feel comfortable asking him questions? Is he a pleasant individual?

A question remains: how does one judge these qualifications in a mohel?

Actually, this is quite the same problem one faces in choosing a good doctor or lawyer. And my advice would be the same. Speak to someone whose business it is to know who is competent and who is not up to recognized halachic standards. The best person to speak to is another competent mohel. This may be impractical in a city which has only one or two mohalim. Discussion with other families who have used the services of a mohel may be helpful in judging certain personal qualities of a mohel, but this is hardly a way to estimate his competence. Discussion with an Orthodox Jewish rabbi might be helpful, since he should know what is happening in his city, especially in this important area of Jewish interest.

If there is no satisfactory mohel, you may be

obligated to ask one to come from another city. This is very costly, but is unfortunately necessary in many parts of the country. The costs involved for having a mohel fly in from another state might be several hundred dollars. This is expensive, but remember that his craftsmanship lasts a lifetime.

The mohel will appreciate being called within a day or two of the child's birth, so he can plan ahead and schedule his time most effectively. He will need to schedule a visit to the baby's home a day or two before the bris, so that he can examine the child and review instructions with the parents.

When I am called by new parents, usually within a few days of the new arrival, I ask about the health of the child at that time, and try to ascertain whether the child is really Jewish. Sad to say, I discover not infrequently that the child's mother or grandmother is not Jewish or has been improperly converted to the Jewish faith. Everything is called off in such a case, although I will refer them to an Orthodox rabbi for further advice on the subject if they so wish. More on this later.

I am also careful to tell them that the bris will be postponed if the child becomes jaundiced. The yellowness which occurs in about 10 percent of newborns is referred to as *physiologic jaundice of the newborn*; and, even though this may represent no illness in the strict sense of the term, it does necessitate postponing the bris milah (see Chapter Fifteen). It is a matter of Jewish law. Even if the child's pediatrician insists that the baby is able to have a circumcision despite the jaundice, a God-fearing mohel who follows the traditions and laws of the Jewish people as they apply to bris milah will not perform a bris until the jaundice lessens or disappears. The bris is also to be postponed in the presence of problems such as fever, significant change in eating habits, or other signs of illness or abnormality.

In addition, I instruct the parents to procure the following items for use during the bris:

1. Fifty 2″ x 2″ sterile gauze pads, individually packaged.
2. One pint 70% isopropyl alcohol.
3. One ounce Bacitracin ointment (a non-prescription item).
4. One bottle of kosher red wine (brand name specified).

I tell them, too, that it would be helpful to have a pillow, some *cloth* diapers, and diaper pins at the bris. I like to have the baby resting on a pillow during the bris. I find it easier to manage cloth diapers during the bris than to have to fool around with the sticky adhesives of the paper diapers when I have half a dozen other things on my mind. I suppose this is mainly a personal preference, but another reason I prefer cloth diapers, certainly for the first 48 hours after a bris, is that air circulation is so much better in a cloth diaper and I feel that this promotes hemostasis and healing.

Although only about ten sterile gauze pads are used during the bris itself, many more will be needed later, since a fresh pad is applied every time the baby has his diaper changed. It is better to have a few too many than to run out of gauze pads in the middle of the night. If the 2″ x 2″ pads are not available at the local drugstore, 3″ x 3″ will do nicely.

The isopropyl alcohol is used by the mohel to soak his instruments before the bris. A good soak in 70% alcohol (either ethyl or isopropyl) will provide as good a sterilization as the boiling of the instruments. I prefer isopropyl alcohol to ethyl (rubbing) alcohol because its odor is less offensive. It may also be a little cheaper. It is my practice to sterilize all my instruments in boiling water at home before the bris. This, in addition to the alcohol soak, assures clean tools with which to work.

The Bacitracin ointment is smeared onto the 2″ x 2″ sterile gauze pad and helps to hold it in place. Many mohalim use A&D ointment and this works quite well. I prefer Bacitracin because it has a stronger antibiotic activity, and although infection is *extremely rare* in a bris milah done in the traditional manner, I feel that this added protection is worth the small expense of the Bacitracin. Neosporin ointment is also acceptable for this purpose, but its purchase requires a doctor's prescription.

In my experience as a mohel, none of my babies has ever had an infection. I have spoken to other mohalim, whose combined experience must total in the thousands or tens of thousands of brissim, and they have never encountered infection. Once, however, a baby circumcised in Canada was brought to me with a superficial infection at the site of the milah about a week after the bris. The treatment I prescribed was merely to bathe the child in warm water a few times a day and to apply Bacitracin ointment to the area. The infection cleared completely in a few days without additional problems.

Considering that the bris milah is performed by mohalim from all sorts of backgrounds—some with much aseptic training, some with none at all; some going to elaborate ends to sterilize their instruments, others merely wiping them with a little hydrogen peroxide or alcohol; some performing *metzitzah* with sterilized glass tubes, others using no instrumentation for this part of the ritual—it is truly wondrous that infection is almost never seen. The traditional answer might be that God protects those who faithfully perform His mitzvos, and I am sure this is true. A medical man, however, might add that the site of the milah is so well supplied with blood vessels—that is, the circulation is so good—that it is almost impossible for an infection to get started. (For the same reason, scalp lacerations almost never become infected. The ample vascularity of the scalp tends to prevent infection.)

A review of the medical literature suggests that infection related to circumcision has become increasingly rare in recent decades. Although it has never been a common problem in Jewish circles, physicians and pathologists have noted instances where a number of maladies were apparently spread via the circumcision wound. These illnesses, if these early reports can be believed, include syphilis, tuberculosis, tetanus, and erysipelas. The reason why these conditions are almost unheard of in relation to ritual circumcision in the past generation or so is probably the fact that the human reservoir for these infections is disappearing. As the infectious diseases themselves are becoming exceedingly rare, so has the possibility of their transmission become almost infinitesimal. In addition, the aseptic technique of the vast majority of the practitioners of ritual circumcision, the mohalim, has improved considerably.

Similarly, medical literature bears out the infrequency of postoperative hemorrhage in ritual circumcision: it occurs in far less than one percent of circumcisions; and, when it does occur, it is usually easily controlled by a reapplication of the dressings by the mohel. Only rarely will a physician have to apply a suture to control bleeding.

Returning now to the supplies which the parents are asked to provide for the bris, there is, lastly, the bottle of wine. Why do I insist on a name brand? Simply to ensure that the wine I ask for is kosher. The Jewish dietary laws concerning wine are quite complicated and strict, and that is why God-fearing Jews drink only wine manufactured under certain labels. The particular wine I request is not the only completely kosher wine, of course; but it is widely available and, in Cleveland, as the distributor has informed me, this brand of wine is *mevushal*, or boiled, which adds an additional degree of *kashrus* protection (as well as sterilization).

So, almost a week before the bris, I have talked with the parents, ascertained that the child is Jewish, warned them about those things that will mean postponing the bris, and instructed them to purchase certain necessary items. Of course, in addition, I always bring a small bottle of wine to a bris, a number of sterile gauze dressings, a pint of isopropyl alcohol, and a tube of Bacitracin, just in case the parents have forgotten anything. You would be surprised to know how much time I have saved with this simple preparation.

Then too, I remind the parents of the tradition of having a little party at home on the Friday night before the bris. This is the *Shalom Zachar* ("welcome, boy") which celebrates the arrival of a new son in the family. If the parents are not observant, I often omit this since I would not want to indirectly cause their relatives and friends to drive on Shabbos.

The *Shalom Zachar* celebration is a very old tradition, whose origins are buried in history. Why Friday night? Some have explained that on Friday night the whole family is home celebrating the Shabbos and that family and friends will have the time to attend. If the bris has to be postponed for some reason, nevertheless, the *Shalom Zachar* is still held on the first Friday night after the birth of the child. Although there is some discussion in rabbinical literature as to whether the *Shalom Zachar* should also be postponed to the Friday night before the bris, the universal practice is to have this celebration on the first Friday night after the birth.

A traditional food served at a *Shalom Zachar* is chick-peas, also called *naheet* or *arbis*. I have asked many people, but have not found a satisfactory explanation for the basis of this tradition. As you may know, we find chick-peas at one other occasion in Jewish life: at the meal served to mourners when they return from the cemetery. The rationale there is that just as the chick-pea has no mouth (its circumference is seamless, unlike many other legumes), so is death silent. Why this same chick-pea at the festive gathering preceding a bris?

There is a tradition that every child while *in utero* is taught the entire Torah by a *malach* (angel). When he is about to be born, he is made to forget this learning. Perhaps it is over this "loss" of Torah that we symbolically "mourn" by eating the chick-pea. Any loss of our sacred traditions, of our holy Torah, is cause for mourning. One of my close friends, presently a teacher at the Telshe Yeshiva, personally knows of a child, born in Israel, who somehow did not forget his learning at the time of his birth: when he learned to talk, he was actually found to know the entire Torah. Such an occurrence caused considerable consternation among his family, and they sought the advice of their Rebbe, who thereupon prayed that the boy should forget this learning so that he might grow great in Torah the normal way, through struggle and work.

We see that even for the vast majority of Jews who remember nothing of their intrauterine existence, becoming knowledgeable in Torah is not really learning anew, but merely recalling, remembering.

11

Other questions before the bris

DURING HIS HOME VISIT on the day before the bris, the mohel has the opportunity to discuss various aspects of the ceremony with which even some observant families are unfamiliar. For example, what furniture will be required for the bris? Where will the Chair of Elijah be stationed? Where will the *sandek* sit? Is there a stool high enough for him, or will the mohel have to provide his own step-stool, as I often do? Where will the mohel be able to place his instruments? Where is the best lighting for the bris?

In addition, many families have to be instructed about the festive meal which follows the bris. This is an opportunity to introduce a non-observant family to the concept of *kashrus*. What the family may be willing to do for this *se'udas mitzvah* might well carry over into their subsequent eating habits.

Another area of ritual which should be reviewed with the new parents by the mohel are the *kibbudim* or honors which can be assigned during the ceremony. There are seven such honors traditionally given to close (Jewish) friends and relatives: **(1)** The *kvatterin* (godmother) brings the baby from the mother (who may wish to remain in another room during the bris) to the door of the room where the bris is to be performed. The baby is taken from her by **(2)** the *kvatter* (godfather), who brings him to **(3)** the one who will place him on the Chair of Elijah (*kisei shel Eliyahu*). The child is then removed from the Chair of Elijah by **(4)** a fourth honored guest and handed to the father. The father hands him to **(5)** the *sandek*, who will hold him during the circumcision itself. After the bris, the baby is taken by **(6)** the one who will hold him while **(7)** another says the *brochos* and the portion of the liturgy giving him his Jewish name. The traditional names for these *kibbudim* are:

1. *Kvatterin* (godmother)
2. *Kvatter* (godfather)
3. *Kisei shel Eliyahu* (Chair of Elijah)
4. *Mi-kisei l'yad ha-av* (from the Chair to the hand of the father)
5. *Sandek* (holds the baby during the bris)
6. *Omed al ha-brocho*, or *sandek sheini* (holds the baby for the blessings and the naming)
7. *Mevoreich* (says the blessings)

Honor (1) goes to a woman; honors (2) through (7), to men only. Needless to say, all participants in a bris must be Jewish.

A chair of carved and painted wood from Darmbach, Thuringia (Germany), 1768. One seat is for the sandek; the other is the kisei shel Eliyahu.

Every now and then a rather unique problem arises. How do you name a child whose father is not Jewish? And who makes the *brocho* then which is usually assigned to the father, "...Who has commanded us to bring him into the Covenant of Abraham our father"?

The child of a non-Jewish father is given its lineage after its mother. For example, if the mother's name is Rivka and the family wants the first name(s) of the baby to be Yitzchok Yaakov, the name given to the child at the bris will be *Yitzchok Yaakov ben Rivka.** If I give the family a certificate of bris milah, I will specify on it that, at the time of the bris, the child's father was not Jewish. There is no need to state that the mother is Jewish, since I maintain a reputation for never performing circumcisions on non-Jewish males. A person's Jewishness depends only on the status of his or her mother, not on the religion of the father.

I usually ask the grandfather (the mother's father) to hand the baby to the *sandek* in place of the (non-Jewish) father during the ceremony. If the grandfather is not present, any Jewish male may substitute. The father's *brocho* is customarily said by the *sandek*. I do not say this *brocho* myself, since at the time of the bris, I am too involved in the actual performance of the surgery to give the *brocho* its proper attention.

I never hesitate to perform such a bris, since this family will need all the help it can get to enable it to achieve some semblance of a Jewish upbringing for this child. Who knows but that the spiritual benefits of having had a properly performed bris milah might not start the child in this direction?

*The child's parent's name is always appended to his/hers to accurately identify and specify that particular Yitzchok Yaakov or Ruth Naomi from all the other Yitzchok Yaakovs and Ruth Naomis in the world.

12

Before the bris

I WOULD LIKE TO DESCRIBE some of the preparation that goes into the performance of a bris which the "customer" may not see. Actually, preparations are begun as soon as I hear from the family. I allot it a morning from my working schedule, and preliminary instructions are given to the parents. Preparations in earnest begin, however, the day before the bris, when I make a home visit to check the health of the child and to acquaint the family with the rudiments of the ceremony they will be hosting the next day.

If the baby is not in perfect health or if he is jaundiced, the bris will be postponed until these problems resolve themselves. More on this in a later chapter.

We decide what will be the best part of the house in which to have the bris. This is usually the living room or dining room, where the space is the most ample and the lighting is the best. We then discuss the various *kibbudim* or honors which will be given to friends and family during the ceremony: who will bring the baby into the room, who will hold him during the bris, who will hold him during the naming ceremony, and so forth. This is a very good time to remind the parents that they will have to choose a Hebrew name for the child. In many families, this reminder precipitates a flurry of phone calls to grandparents, aunts and uncles, not only to find an appropriate name for the baby boy but occasionally even to ascertain the correct Hebrew name of the father! If there is indecision, I sometimes will suggest a first name which is somehow related to the portion of the Torah being read in *shul* that week—for example, Avraham at the portion of *Lech Lecha*.

One mother complained to me indignantly, "But I don't like the name Ben for my son." Patiently, I explained to her that *ben* means "son of" and is the common property of all Jewish men, just as *bas* (daughter of) would be found in the names of all Jewish women. (For example: Yitzchok ben Avraham, "Isaac son of Abraham.")

I do not spend too much time during this first home visit discussing the post-operative care of the child. This is more effectively done after the bris, when I can actually demonstrate to the mother the proper care of the incision.

I do not forget to ask the parents to show me the supplies which I asked them to purchase for the bris when they first called me: the sterile gauze dressings, the pint of 70% isopropyl alcohol, the ounce tube of

Bacitracin antibiotic ointment, and the bottle of kosher red wine.

On the morning of the bris I get up very early. While most of the world is still sound asleep, I drive to one of our community's *mikvaos* (ritual baths) and immerse myself while concentrating on the importance of the mitzvah which I have been asked to perform. The mohel asks Divine assistance and guidance in the proper and careful performance of this great precept.

After the *mikvah*, I proceed to the *shul*, where I join the *minyan* in the traditional morning services. An observant Jew is seen in his *shul* three times daily: in the morning, the late afternoon, and evening; and any mohel who takes his work seriously also takes all aspects of his Jewish living seriously, including congregational worship. A congregation is happy to have a mohel *daven* (worship) in its midst, since the services are considerably shortened when he is present and has a bris to perform later in the day. Certain parts of the morning service called *Tachnunim*, supplications, are omitted on account of the general air of celebration which accompanies the performance of a bris in the community.

Since it is an age-old custom among mohalim not to eat or drink before performing a bris, the mohel does not return home from *shul* for breakfast but goes directly to the house where the bris will occur. If the bris is scheduled for the afternoon, I have breakfast, because if I fast for more than half the day I feel that I cannot work at my best.

When I arrive at the house or synagogue where the ceremony is to take place, I get my equipment ready. I insert my instruments in a container filled with the isopropyl alcohol, which the family has purchased for me. The knife has already been sharpened and all the instruments have been sterilized in boiling water the evening before. While the instruments are soaking, I set a clean paper covering on a small table which has been placed next to the chair on which the *sandek* will hold the baby during the bris. On this clean surface I arrange my dressings and instruments.

A few minutes before the bris, I will visit the baby one last time, to prepare him for the surgery by gently probing under the foreskin with a lubricated silver probe. This greatly facilitates the performance of the milah itself, and I always do it in the presence of the father or mother. Every now and then you may hear people complaining that a mohel "did everything in the bedroom." To squelch such rumors, I explain to the parents exactly what I am doing and let them see clearly that this is nothing more than preparation for the actual bris.

At this time, I spend a few moments with the child's father reviewing the blessing he will say during the ceremony right after the foreskin is removed. In English, this blessing is: "Blessed are You, Lord our God, King of the universe, Who has sanctified us with His commandments and commanded us to bring this child into the Covenant of Abraham our father."

Finally, we are ready to begin. I regard it almost as a point of honor to have my brissim start on or very close to the time I have arranged with the family, so I advise them to tell their relatives and friends to be there at least fifteen minutes before I plan to actually start the bris.

Now there are three minutes to go. The living room is full of people. My instruments are prepared and arranged. The baby is getting his final diaper change upstairs in his bedroom. I take off my suit coat and turn off the radiopage ("beeper") that I always carry, so that it will not start beeping and interrupt the bris.

Because I go to great lengths to emphasize to the people gathered that what they are about to see is a religious matter and not merely a cosmetic surgical procedure, I always wear a *gartel* and a large woolen *tallis*, which I don (with a *brocho*) just before we start. A final washing of the hands completes my preparations.

I ask that the *kvatterin* (godmother) bring the child to the entrance of the room where the bris will be performed and hand him to the *kvatter* (godfather), who then brings him to me. Everyone welcomes the baby with the traditional "*Boruch ha-ba*" (blessed is he who comes). I continue with the traditional introduction to the bris, in Hebrew: "And God spoke to Moses saying: Pinchas the son of Elazar the son of Aaron the Priest has turned away My anger from the Children of Israel because he was very jealous for My sake among them, so that I did not consume the Children of Israel in My jealousy. Therefore say: Behold I give unto him My covenant of peace" (*Bemidbar*/Numbers 25:10-12).

The man who has been assigned the honor of taking the child from the *kvatter* and placing him on the *kisei shel Eliyahu* (chair reserved for Elijah the Prophet) brings the baby to the chair which has been so designated for this purpose. Before he places the child on it, the mohel continues (in Hebrew): "This is the chair of Elijah, may he be remembered for good! For Your salvation I have waited, Lord. I have hoped, Lord, for Your salvation and have done Your commandments. Elijah, messenger of the bris, behold your reward is before you. Stand by my right hand and support me. (O Lord) I rejoice at Your word as one who finds great gain. Great peace have they who love Your Torah and there is no stumbling for them. Happy is he whom You have chosen to bring close to dwell in Your courts. May we be satisfied with the goodness of Your House, Your Holy Temple."

A single chair, highly ornamented, used for decades as the kisei shel Eliyahu *by the Jewish community of Rome.*

13

After the bris

THE ACTUAL PERFORMANCE of the milah, the surgical part of the bris, is straightforward. Although there are several techniques used by God-fearing mohalim, they all share certain basic similarities. This mohel may use a shield in addition to his knife and probe. Another may add a hemostat. A third may forgo all instrumentation, using only the traditional *izmel*.

While the father is handing the infant to the *sandek*, I utter under my breath a short *tefillah* (prayer), "The Holy One blessed be He said to Abraham our father: *Go before Me and be whole (in faith)*. Here I stand ready and prepared to fulfill the positive commandment which the blessed Creator has commanded me—to circumcise."

As I adjust the position of the child, who is resting on a pillow in the lap of the *sandek*, I remind the father of the infant that the mitzvah of bris milah is really *his mitzvah*, and I am merely serving as his deputy. Since he has not had the experience in the performance of the technical aspects of the mitzvah, he has asked me to do the surgery. Sometimes, I will add emphasis to this relationship by handing the knife to the father so that he may pass it to me at the proper time. This concretizes the legal relationship which must exist between the two of us in the eyes of *halachah*, the Jewish law.

The baby is now resting on the *sandek*'s lap, his legs facing me. The *sandek* is to hold the feet apart, flexing and externally rotating the hips to give me a good operating field. It is important that he hold the thighs far apart so that there is no risk of them (or the *sandek*'s thumbs) being nicked during the bris.

I place a few paper towels under the child's buttocks to minimize the amount of blood that might stain the diapers. These towels are discarded right after the bris, before the diaper pins are fastened. An additional advantage in using paper towels in this fashion is that a bowel movement (and this has happened during a bris more than once) need not necessitate a change of diapers. The towels are merely thrown away and replaced.

We are ready to start the milah. I grasp the foreskin and draw it forward. Then I place the shield over the foreskin between my fingers and the glans penis, angling it to the degree that I want my incision to transect the tissue. While I am doing this I start the *brocho* which I will finish just prior to removing the foreskin with the knife, which the father is now holding:

"Blessed are You, King of the universe, Who has sanctified us with His commandments and has commanded us concerning milah."

The foreskin is removed with a single cut from the razor-sharp *izmel* and the shield falls off. I carefully place the foreskin, knife, and shield on the table next to me and observe the genitalia. Was enough foreskin removed? How much of the mucosal membrane remains? Is there much bleeding, and from where?

I then firmly grasp with my sharpened thumbnails the mucosal tissue covering the glans penis, and split it in the midline, drawing the two halves backward, off the glans, and set them on the shaft of the penis. Now, one must carefully inspect his work to ascertain that all the mucosal layer has been peeled off the glans and that there are no skin tags or adhesions (*tzitzin*) remaining.

The first step of the milah is called *chituch* and consists of removing the prepuce. The second step, called *priah*, involves the splitting and peeling back of the mucosal surface (*or hapriah*), thus uncovering the surface of the glans penis (*atorah*). The third step, *metzitzah*, is the drawing out of excess blood from the wound, accomplished by the mouth or with a hollow glass cylinder which fits over the penis and through which gentle suction can be applied. All three steps are essential for the proper performance of the bris, and a mohel who neglects any one of these steps should be dismissed from his responsibilities.

The final part of the operative procedure is the bandaging; and there are a great many different techniques to accomplish this. I wrap the wound snugly with a ½" x 12" strip of gauze and place a few 2" x 2" sterile gauze pads over this before replacing the diaper. Many mohalim use a variety of hemostatic powders, but I have not found this necessary. A carefully placed dressing is usually enough to achieve adequate hemostasis.

The baby is rewrapped in the clothing which he wore to the bris, and is handed to the person who will have the honor of holding him during the naming.

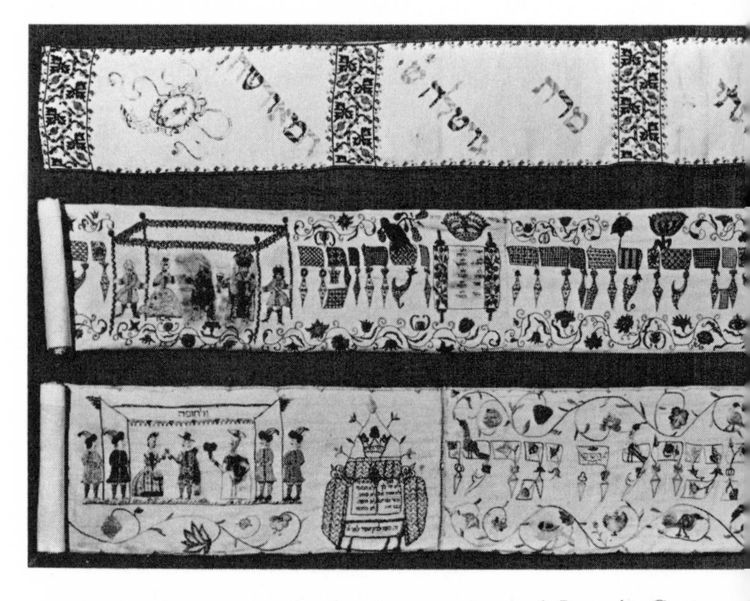

In previous centuries it was a custom of Jews in German and Italy to have a child circumcised on a linen cloth, an later the cloth was cut into four strips and made into a lon sash, to be used for tying a Torah scroll in the synagogue Embroidered with silk thread (generally by the mother), i gave the child's name and birthdate, and the blessing tha

This is an important honor, second only to that of the *sandek*, and is indeed sometimes referred to as *sandek sheini* (the second *sandek*).

If the family's rabbi is present, he will usually pronounce the *brochos* which are said after the bris, and will then give the baby the Hebrew name. If no rabbi is present I will have this honor.

First I fill the goblet over which the *brocho* will be said (usually provided by myself) with wine. It is important to rinse this goblet with water and wipe it

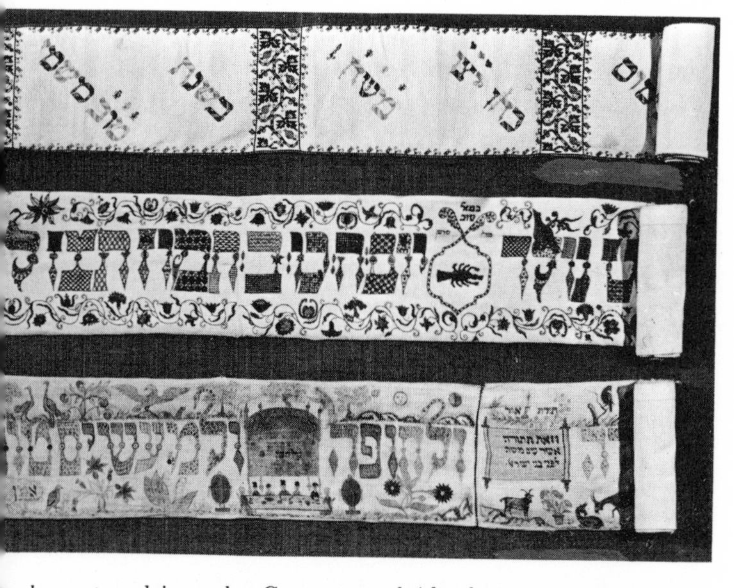

s he entered into the Covenant of Abraham, so may he ter into Torah, marriage and good deeds." A wedding ene could thus be added ("into... marriage"). It was con-crated for use with a Torah scroll upon the child's first try into the synagogue, or at his bar mitzvah. These amples date from the 17th to the 19th centuries.

dry before the bris in accordance with Jewish practice. Whenever making a *brocho* over wine, you should use a cup or glass which has been especially cleaned and prepared for this purpose.

The first *brocho* is: "Blessed are You, Lord our God, King of the universe, Who has created the fruit of the vine."

The mohel (or rabbi) continues: "Blessed are You, Lord our God, King of the universe, Who from the womb did make beloved Isaac holy, and Who placed Your commandment in his flesh, and sealed his offspring with the sign of the holy bris. Because of this, O Living God, our Portion and our Rock, give command to save from destruction the dearly beloved of our flesh, for the sake of the bris which You have placed in our flesh. Blessed are You, O Lord, Who makes the Covenant."

The *brocho* having now been said for the wine and for the bris milah itself, the mohel (or whoever is saying the *brochos*) now proceeds to give the baby boy his Jewish name:

"Our God and God of our fathers, maintain this child for his father and mother, and let his name be called in Israel *so-and-so* son of *so-and-so*. Let the father rejoice in his offspring and the mother be glad with the fruit of her womb, as it is written: Let the father and mother rejoice, and let her who gave birth to you be glad (*Mishlei*/Proverbs 23:25). And it is said: Then I passed by you, and I saw you weltering in your blood, and I said to you, *In your blood live, in your blood live* (*Yechezkel*/Ezekiel 16:6). And it is said: He has remembered His covenant forever, the word which He commanded to a thousand generations, the covenant which He made with Abraham, and His oath to Isaac, and He confirmed it to Jacob as a statute, to Israel as an eternal covenant (*Tehillim*/Psalms 105:8-10). And it is said: And Abraham circumcised his son Isaac when he was eight days old, as God commanded him (*Bereishis*/Genesis 21:4). Give thanks to the Lord for He is good, for His kindness is forever. Give thanks to the Lord for He is good, for His kindness is forever (*Tehillim*/Psalms 118:1). May this small child, *so-and-so* son of *so-and-so*, become great. Just as he has been entered into the Covenant, may he enter the world of the Torah, the marriage canopy, and the practice of good deeds."

I sip a few drops of wine from the goblet and send the remainder off to the mother, according to ancient custom. I then recite a prayer for the rapid recovery of the child and conclude with *Aleinu* (the prayer which concludes every Jewish prayer service), after which the mourner's *kaddish* may be said if there are any in attendance who are saying *kaddish* for a departed relative.

This concludes the bris, and a *mazal tov* is in order for one and all. Another link has been forged in the chain which extends back into history to Abraham himself, almost four thousand years ago.

While the visitors are preparing to sit down to the *se'udah* which has been prepared for them, I clean my instruments and put them away. I leave everything

Two identically decorated cups of beaten and chased silver, with mouths that fit together for compact carrying. The letters on the upper cup denote kos shel metzitzah*: into it the mohel emitted the excess blood that he drew off by suction. The letters on the lower one mean* kos shel brocho*: It was filled with wine, and over it the blessings were recited. Made in Germany between 1712 and 1721.*

the way I found it, so as to leave nothing for the family to have to clean up after me. I place a note on the Chair of Elijah requesting that people not use this chair or move it for three days—according to custom. Everyone is always quite willing to accede to this request.

I then see the baby to change the dressings. The gauze which I put on at the time of the bris is removed and the wound checked carefully for excessive bleeding. A fresh sterile gauze wrapping similar to the first is applied, and perhaps a drop of Adrenalin, which I feel may minimize mucosal swelling and also provide some greater measure of hemostasis. However, it is important to remember that in addition to the natural tendency of cut surfaces to stop bleeding and to heal, 90% of further hemostasis is the result of proper bandaging: it should be not too tight to restrict the circulation or the flow of urine, but also not too loose. The skin edges must be properly aligned for rapid healing, and a high level of hygiene must be maintained to minimize the possibilities of infection. Of all the skills of a mohel, a proper and effective application of the dressings is one of the hardest to learn.

While I am changing the dressings, I explain to the parents or the nurse, if there is one in attendance, what their main responsibilities are during the next three or four days, while healing is taking place.

First of all, they must not touch the circularly applied dressing. I will return the next morning (or the next evening, if the following day is Shabbos) and remove it. Each time they change a diaper they will be responsible for changing the 2″ x 2″ sterile gauze dressing which is placed over the end of the penis. A small amount of antibiotic ointment is smeared on this small square dressing before application. This not only provides a degree of antibiotic protection but also allows for easy changing of the dressing, since it forms a non-sticking lubrication between the dressing and the wound.

Second, the family is told to be aware of signs of significant bleeding. This may be bright red blood which stains the diapers over an area of several square inches. Anything less than this is not significant and may be ignored. I describe to them the appearance of urine which has soaked up some of the blood in the dressings, so that they will not be alarmed by the appearance of pink staining in the diapers.

If the child does not urinate within four hours or so after the bris, this is something the mohel would like to know. There are rare instances, described in the medical literature, of problems arising from too tight an application of the circular dressing around the circumcision incision.

I caution the parents to expect some crankiness and restlessness on the part of the child during the first night after the bris, but assure them that this will usually pass after the dressing is removed in the morning. I suspect that the fresh circumcision and the irritation of the dressings cause the child some discomfort. However, healing is rapid and the child will be able to undergo normal cleaning procedures such as sponging or baths 48 hours after the bris. Except for a little swelling (and sometimes not even swelling is present), complete healing usually occurs within a week.

Finally, I ask the parents not to hesitate to call me at any time of day or night if they think they may need help. If there is bleeding or any other problem, I want to know about it right away. Fortunately, though, problems are extremely rare.

I return the next morning and carefully remove the long gauze dressing. It is usually bleached white by the child's urine, and comes off quite easily. With the removal of the last turn of the gauze, the part actually touching the raw surface of the circumcision wound, the baby cries a little, and there are often a few drops of blood from the skin edges. However, this always stops by itself and presents no problems.

At this final meeting with the parents, I bring up the fact that in today's world a Jewish education is necessary for survival and mention several options both for the parents and the child in terms of increasing their involvement in a more Jewish way of life. Fathers and mothers are usually very receptive to this line of thinking, but I suppose only time will tell if such advice will bear fruit.

14

Have knife, will travel

WHEN I FIRST BECAME A MOHEL, I was not inclined to accept invitations to perform brissim beyond the greater Cleveland area, and I still hesitate to travel too far from home. This is not entirely in accordance with the practice of many mohalim who will travel great distances to perform this sacred mitzvah. I know of a case where a mohel has flown to South America to perform a bris, and I am sure this is not a rare occurrence.

My professional obligations as a physician, however, do not allow me the luxury of taking off as much time as I would like in order to officiate at ritual circumcisions more than a thirty-minute drive from my home. As I have mentioned, I like to see the baby on the day before the bris to determine whether or not he is healthy enough to undergo the milah. The following day is the bris itself. And on the day afterward, I return to remove the dressings and check the status of the operation. It is thus a matter of three days.

In the past year, though, I have made several exceptions to this rule and have traveled some distance to do brissim. The lack of qualified mohalim in the Midwest has made this necessary. Although I have helped train several young men in the art of the craft, it requires some time before they are ready to go out on their own.

Because I will have the opportunity in such cases to see the baby only once, on the day of the bris itself, I speak to the family and to the pediatrician beforehand to determine whether or not all criteria for going ahead with the bris have been met. I ask the doctor if the child is at all jaundiced. I find out what the serum bilirubin is and whether it is rising or falling (about this see the next chapter). I inform the parents that if for some reason I do not feel I can perform the bris when I arrive, the bris will have to be postponed.

In addition, I try to arrange to stay with the family of the child for at least four hours after the bris, to be able to rewrap the bandage if there should be any excessive bleeding. As far as making provisions for removing the dressing the following morning, I instruct the father or the pediatrician how to remove it carefully.

The following is an account of one such affair I attended beyond the Cleveland area. It took place in Akron and was written up by Mr. Charles Rost, a free-lance writer, who has kindly allowed me to incorporate his eye-witness account (in abridged form) in this chapter. As you will see, the bris was unusual in a number of respects.

TRIPLETS IN AKRON

A bris (ritual circumcision) is always a joyous event in a Jewish household since it represents the initiation of the newly born Jewish male into the age-old covenant between the Jewish people and God. Even among families who are not as aware of Jewish traditions, this rite has deep meaning and is adhered to even after other forms of traditional observance have been forgotten. So you can imagine the joy with which the Aronson family celebrated the bris of their triplets this past Sunday, February 26th. The ceremony was performed at the Beth El Synagogue in Akron by Dr. Henry Romberg, a physician and mohel (ritual circumcisor) from Cleveland.

The Aronsons, who have been married for ten years and have been childless until recently, were understandably surprised, but thankful, for this triple blessing, the answer to many years of prayer and hope. The mother, Esther Aronson, an education specialist in the Akron public schools, understands that taking care of triplets is not the same as taking care of three children born in the normal sequence—since all the infants, being the same age, will have the same urgent needs *at the same time*. She knows she will have the help and support of her husband, Ronald, a manager of a tire firm in Cuyahoga Falls. Both parents are thirty years old.

TRIPLE CIRCUMCISION

Although the babies were born December 20th at the Akron City Hospital, the ritual circumcision had to be postponed several months because the size and health of the infants did not permit the performance on the eighth day, which is the Jewish practice. Dr. Romberg, the mohel, explained that although it is a Biblical commandment to circumcise a Jewish male on the eighth day after birth (for example, if the child is born on Thursday, the bris will take place on the following Thursday), the circumcision is postponed if the baby is jaundiced, underweight, or in any way ill. The Aronson children were born six weeks prematurely, were all underweight, and two of them suffered pulmonary complications requiring intensive care at Akron's Children's Hospital. Dr. Romberg explained that the laws and traditions concerning the postponement of a bris are very detailed, and they ensure that no chance whatsoever is taken which might endanger the health of an infant.

Dr. Romberg told me he had come to Akron once before, to circumcise a five-year-old Russian boy whose family had recently left the Soviet Union. The bris was done in the hospital, with the child under light anesthesia.

"I have performed bris milah on adults in my office or in the home under local anesthesia," Dr. Romberg said, "but most ritual circumcision on adults is now done in Cleveland in the operating rooms of the Mount Sinai Hospital, which generously donates its services and facilities so that this mitzvah can be performed without cost for these poor Jewish immigrants from Russia."

THE CEREMONY

Returning to Sunday's happy events, the triple circumcision at Akron's Beth El Synagogue, Dr. Romberg explained, "The ceremony itself consists of three parts. First the child is welcomed into the room where the bris is to be performed. The mohel welcomes the child, in Hebrew, then directs that he be placed on the 'Chair of Elijah the Prophet,' who traditionally attends every bris, just as he attends every Passover Seder. At Passover, a cup of wine is reserved for the prophet, but at a bris, there is a chair reserved for him. Then the child is taken from the Chair of Elijah and handed to the father. The father hands him to the *sandek*, usually the infant's grandfather. This completes the first part of the ritual."

Since there were three young brothers to be circumcised, and since Jewish tradition discourages a *sandek* from officiating more than once in the same family, there were three men honored with this pleasant task at the ceremony: the maternal grandfather, who lives in Akron; the paternal grandfather, who flew in from Phoenix, Arizona; and an uncle from Brooklyn, New York. Both Rabbi Feffer and Rabbi Liebtag took part in the ceremonies.

The second stage of the ceremony is the circumcision itself. Dr. Romberg, wearing the traditional prayer shawl or *tallis*, performed the operation swiftly and expertly, using instruments which might have been used thousands of years ago.

The circumcision completed, the infant was handed to another man while the rabbi said the blessings over a silver goblet of wine and gave the child his Jewish name, the name he will henceforth be known by in the Jewish community. This concluded the third and final stage of the ceremony.

After the bris, a feast was served to the more than three hundred and fifty guests present. The food was tasty and plentiful. No wonder, since one of the grandparents operates Akron's kosher catering facilities.

The birth of triplets is a rare occurrence in Akron. This bris will be remembered for a long time by the Jewish community of that city.

15

When your newborn is yellow

WHAT IS PHYSIOLOGIC JAUNDICE?

ONE OF THE MORE CONFUSING AREAS of pediatric physiology, from the layman's point of view, is the area which physicians call *physiologic jaundice of the newborn* and which everyone else refers to simply as jaundice or yellowness. It occurs frequently, and often postpones a bris beyond the eighth day.

First and foremost, I want to emphasize that in the vast majority of cases, jaundice in the newborn does not signify disease or abnormality of any sort. Though it is true that there are a number of dangerous conditions which can trigger jaundice in this age-group, such as a systemic infection or several types of liver disease, ninety-nine jaundiced babies out of a hundred will merely be exhibiting a variation of the normal and will return to the average appearance of all other infants in a few days or weeks.

What, then, is physiologic jaundice of the newborn? First, *physiologic* means that the condition is not a disease but merely a reflection of normal processes. I shall explain what these normal processes are a bit further on.

Jaundice refers to a yellowish cast of the skin which occurs when an organic dye known as *bilirubin* accumulates in the blood and is deposited in the tissues. When red blood cells break down in the blood stream, they release their red pigment (which is called *hemoglobin—hemo* is the actual pigment, *globin* is the complex protein to which it is attached). The hemoglobin breaks down in a number of steps to bilirubin, which, before it is acted upon by the liver, is called *unconjugated bilirubin*. After it passes through the liver, it becomes attached to another molecule and is now referred to as *conjugated bilirubin*.

Red blood cells are breaking down in the human body all the time. In the normal adult, a red cell will live for approximately 120 days. That is to say, the bone marrow (where red blood cells originate) has to manufacture every day 1/120th of the entire red cell population in the body. The pigments released by non-functional red cells are converted to bilirubin, which is then picked up by the liver, converted to conjugated bilirubin, and passed out via the bile ducts into the small intestine, where it imparts the characteristic brown color to the stool.

If the bile ducts are obstructed (as, for example, by a gallstone) or if the liver is not operating efficiently (as in hepatitis or alcoholic cirrhosis), or if the blood cells are dissolving at a greatly increased rate (as in certain hemolytic anemias), the bile-pigment bilirubin will back up into the blood and appear in the tissues in the form of jaundice. In severe jaundice, even the whites of the eyes become yellow, and this condition is known as icterus.

In newborns, not only is the rate of red cell production and destruction much greater than in the adult, but in addition, the yet immature liver is often unable to pass out all the bilirubin which is presented to it. It may be even less able to do so if it is simultaneously presented with other substances to process, such as certain hormones found in the mother's milk.

Because of these factors, actually only slight exaggerations of the normal situation, a mild jaundice may occasionally occur. Sometimes, however, the degree of jaundice can become so severe that medical intervention will be required. But generally, the jaundice will recede of its own accord as the infant's own liver matures and becomes more able to handle the bilirubin load presented to it.

Nevertheless, since we are not always sure of the cause of the jaundice—even though the pediatrician may assure us that the condition is the self-limited physiologic variety—Jewish law prohibits a mohel from operating until the jaundice disappears almost completely. Physiologic jaundice of the newborn usually recedes sufficiently to allow a bris in one or two weeks after the date of the postponement.

To emphasize how important it is to heed the advice of the mohel, I would like to mention one case of an infant who was jaundiced. I was not the mohel, but I was called on, both in my capacity as a mohel and as a physician, to advise the family on whether or not to postpone this bris.

The child appeared well in every respect, except that he was somewhat yellow. The family doctor had said it would be safe to proceed with the ritual circumcision, but the family's mohel was hesitant. I advised the family that, although I could understand the thinking of the physician, Jewish tradition was clear on this point: the bris of a jaundiced infant is postponed, even though this might cause some inconvenience to relatives who may have flown in from other parts of the country.

In the end, this bris was postponed. A few days afterward, the child broke out in a disseminated staphylococcal infection, which resulted in the postponement of the bris for a full month. This infection certainly had not occurred overnight and must have been brewing for several days. The child's jaundice was the only indication that something was very wrong. Serious complications might have resulted had the bris been performed on the day it was originally scheduled.

There is no unanimity among mohalim as to what constitutes an acceptable degree of jaundice (since a skilled eye can detect a trace of yellowness in the majority of newborns). Many mohalim rely on their training and experience to make this determination, and this is indeed the traditional method, since a great part of a mohel's apprenticeship is involved in examining babies to determine whether they are fit to be circumcised. Other mohalim rely also on the bilirubin level in the baby's blood as determined by laboratory tests.

Others, again, will postpone a bris whenever the child appears yellow no matter what the level of the serum bilirubin is, and yet will circumcise a child of normal appearance if the pediatrician permits it, even if the bilirubin as measured by the laboratory is elevated.

I generally rely on the appearance of the infant. If the parents are dark complexioned, I am sometimes uncertain whether the hue of the infant is a result of the genetic inheritance of skin color or is related to an elevated bilirubin level. In such a case, I will request a serum bilirubin (a laboratory examination), and will postpone the bris if it is above 7 mg% (milligrams of bilirubin per 100 milliliters of serum). Other mohalim use the figure of 6 mg%. There is a respected opinion which holds that once a bris is postponed because of an elevated bilirubin, one must wait until the bilirubin drops to normal levels before doing the bris.

There are other medical matters which will cause a ritual circumcision to be postponed. First, I would emphasize that the pediatrician plays a vital role in the postponement of a bris. Under Jewish law, if the medical doctor says that the bris should be postponed, it *must* be postponed. This does not depend upon whether the physician is Jewish or not Jewish, religious or not religious. The law is very clear on this point. If there is any reason to suspect danger to the child, the circumcision is postponed, for "A milah can be performed at a later date, but the life of a Jewish child can never be restored" (*Code of Jewish Law*). Therefore, if the doctor feels that there is even the slightest danger to the child, we do not hesitate to postpone the circumcision.

On the other hand we also follow the stringencies of Jewish tradition (in the matter of jaundice, for example) and postpone the bris even if a hundred doctors say that there is no danger to the child. This is not an infrequent occurrence. The pediatrician will often tell the parents of a slightly jaundiced child that it is perfectly all right to go ahead with the bris. The family then asks me why I am postponing the bris, when the physician said it would be perfectly safe to have it on time. Perhaps it is fortunate in these circumstances that I, too, am a physician and can defend my position not only as a mohel but as a medical doctor. It is a sad commentary on the state of Jewish life in America that even some Orthodox couples are sometimes inclined to depart from Jewish law and tradition in this vital area that involves the health of their own child.

Incidentally, it has been my experience that it is so much easier to postpone a bris on account of jaundice if I have previously explained this possibility to the parents when they first call me. Indeed, this often puts them on the lookout for the appearance of jaundice, which will usually occur on or about the fourth day after birth.

In addition to examining the child for jaundice, there are other reasons why the mohel makes a house call a day or so before the bris. He must also see if the child is completely normal in other ways. There are certain abnormalities of the genitalia which will necessitate a slightly different technique of circumcision (such as a very small penis or a minimal hypospadias). Other abnormalities will require a postponement of the circumcision. In these cases the mohel will always consult with the pediatrician or urologist.

The visit the day before the bris is very important, since the mohel can much more objectively suggest medical consultation to the parents then, rather than if he sees the infant for the first time at the ceremony, surrounded by a crowd of anxious relatives and well-wishers. And most pediatricians and urologists, realizing the importance of having a ritual circumcision on the eighth day, will usually arrange to see the child immediately if their advice is sought by the family and the mohel.

Top: *a milah book (parchment manuscript) with the text for the ceremony, embellished with a circumcision scene (from Hamburg-Altona, Germany 1729).* Underneath, left: *a cup to be filled with earth, to receive the foreskin; the cup beneath it is the cover (Germany, 18th century).* Right: *a flask for a healing powder, which was sprinkled over the wound (silver; Italy, 19th century).* Below them: *a milah knife of steel, silver and amber (Near East 1819).* Bottom: *a circumcision shield from 19th-century France.*

16

Is the baby Jewish?

It would certainly be hard to say how many non-Jewish children are ritually circumcised each year in the United States. The number may be large and, if the mohel is not careful, he may indeed find himself circumcising gentiles. As the rate of intermarriage climbs, this problem is bound to increase.

What is wrong with performing a ritual circumcision on a non-Jew? First and foremost, it is simply against the Jewish law. It is not permitted. A Jew is allowed to circumcise a gentile only for reasons of health. That is, if there is a medical reason for a non-Jew needing to have his foreskin removed, such as inflammation, inability to retract the prepuce, or painful sexual relations because of an abnormally developed or diseased foreskin, then a Jewish doctor would be allowed to remove this piece of anatomy as a medical procedure, but not as a part of a ritual reserved for the Jewish people.

In most instances, the mohel will find himself in the situation of having circumcised a non-Jew because at the time, he was unaware that the child was not Jewish. No mohel worthy of the profession would knowingly circumcise a non-Jewish baby unless he had permission from the *Beis Din* (Jewish court) in his community to do so as a preparation for the formal conversion of the child to Judaism. In such a situation, different blessings are said at the time of the milah, and the ritual is also slightly different.

Very early in my career as a mohel I learned to ask questions in order to ascertain the pedigree of the child whom I was being asked to enter into the Covenant of Abraham. To my knowledge, I have never ritually circumcised anyone who was not Jewish.

Perhaps it would be reasonable here to discuss the question "Who is a Jew?" This is an important matter to understand because it is of utmost importance and interest to every Jew in the world. It is not only a problem for the Israeli immigration authorities — whom to admit to the State of Israel under the Law of Return, which guarantees admission to the Land of Israel to anyone who is Jewish. It is a matter which is important for you and for me. Who is that person our child may be marrying someday? Is he or she really Jewish, or merely travelling under a false identity — usually through no fault of his or her own but because someone simply did not know all the facts a generation or two ago.

At the outset, we should agree that being Jewish is not simply what you or I think should be Jewish. The definition of Jewishness is not up to you or me to make. It is a theological definition. "Who is a Jew" is one who God says is Jewish—simply that. And to know what God says on the subject, we must turn to His Torah. The Jewish law, derived from the Torah communicated to the Jewish people through Moses, defines a Jew as one who has been born of a Jewish mother or has converted to Judaism according to the rigorous precepts of the Jewish law, the *halachah.*

Therefore, if the father is Jewish and the mother is not, the child is a non-Jew. If the mother is Jewish and the father a gentile, the child is completely Jewish. If the mother has been converted to Judaism by a Reform or Conservative rabbi, or through a defective "Orthodox" procedure, her children are not Jewish. If a child who is not Jewish is raised thinking he or she is Jewish, is the recipient of a fine Jewish education, and considers him/herself Jewish in every way, that person is still not Jewish. *Jewish* is, simply and plainly, being born of a Jewish mother or being converted to Judaism according to the *halachah* (traditional Law). There are no exceptions. Anyone who tells you differently is either ignorant or a charlatan.

Not too long ago, a Jewish grandmother called me up to do a bris on her grandson who had been born earlier in the day. She had attended a bris I had performed earlier that year and liked my style. Now it was her turn, and she wanted to make sure I would hold the date open for her new grandson.

She was obviously Jewish. There was a Yiddish

flavor to her English. Therefore the son, too, was Jewish. But that does not count, since it is the infant's mother who determines the Jewishness of the child. I have performed a number of brissim where the father was not Jewish. This does not matter: if the mother is Jewish, the child is Jewish. There is no such thing as a half-Jew in the eyes of the Law.

Now, before I had a chance to ask about the child's mother, the lady I was speaking to volunteered the information that, although it was her son's first child, her daughter-in-law had an eleven-year-old girl by a previous marriage.

Red flags started to go up in my mind.

"Let me ask you, Mrs. So-and-so," I said. "Is your daughter-in-law Jewish?"

"No, Dr. Romberg," she answered a little hesitantly.

That was good news and bad news: good news, as I shall clarify in a moment, because it meant that her grandchild was not a *mamzer*, illegitimate in the eyes of the Law and forever forbidden to marry within the Jewish fold; bad news, because there would be no bris. The child was in no way Jewish. How was I going to break the news to her?

(Let me hasten to add here that although the laws which declare a person Jewish or not are relatively simple to understand, those involving the category of *mamzer* are complex. Whether a person is a *mamzer* or not is a question that *must* be brought before an Orthodox rabbi who is competent to discuss these matters.)

"Mrs. So-and-so," I explained, "because your daughter-in-law is not Jewish, your grandson is not Jewish.

"But you have a lot to be happy about," I added quickly. "You should be very happy. Because she is not Jewish, the only problem is one of a proper conversion for her and her son. If she had been Jewish, previously married to another Jewish man and not properly divorced, then your grandson would be in real trouble."

I did not go into the details about *mamzer* with her. Enough had been said, and she would be unable to comprehend more.

"But my son's Jewish," she stammered.

"I'm sorry. It's a woman's world here. The child's Jewishness is entirely dependent on the mother," I said gently but forcefully. "The father can be the biggest rabbi in the world, but if the mother is a gentile, the child is a gentile."

There was no bris.

I explained to this distraught grandmother that the mother and child would have to be converted to Judaism according to Orthodox practices, and that any other conversion would not be worth the paper it was written on. I gave her the name of the head of the Board of Orthodox Rabbis in Cleveland, feeling sure that he would explain to her and her daughter-in-law the details of conversion if that was what they sincerely wanted.

Before I dismissed the whole sad incident from my mind, I called the other mohel in Cleveland, explained the situation to him, and gave him the name of the parents. It has been my experience that a family for whom I have refused — on halachic grounds — to be the mohel, will often call another mohel and conceal the true facts of the situation from him. He appreciated my calling and thanked me. With that done, my job was finished.

It is indeed unfortunate that so many well-meaning but unlearned Jews get themselves into difficulties of this sort because (1) they do not know what the Jewish law says on the matter; or (2) they are misled by their "rabbis" who are either unlearned themselves in the Law or are purposely trying to mislead them for their own personal motives, or who hold the mistaken belief that they are protecting them from unhappiness.

You might wonder perhaps why I really could not perform a circumcision on a child who was not Jewish (but whose parents thought he was). I could just not say the blessings. It would be a simple surgical circumcision. Certainly such an intermarried family would not know the difference. Indeed, many families which I visit would not know anything about bris milah if I did not explain what I was doing every step of the way.

There are some mohalim who would circumcise a child under the pretense that they were doing it *l'shem geirus*. That is, they would have in mind that if this child would ever wish to convert sometime in the future, the first step of the *geirus* or conversion, the ritual circumcision, would have been completed.

Either alternative—doing a cosmetic circumcision without the *brochos*, or performing a *milah l'shem geirus*—rests on very shaky halachic grounds. In the first case, it is not permitted by Jewish law to perform a circumcision on a gentile except under very specific circumstances. In the second case, to perform the circumcision *l'shem geirus*, it is highly improbable that such a family will ever come to a proper conversion, and one is merely blurring the distinction between the Jewish people and the rest of the world by indiscriminately circumcising gentiles. Let such a child be circumcised by a physician in the hospital, and then, in the future, let him approach a properly constituted *Beis Din* for conversion. The mohel, an official representative of the Jewish people and the Torah, should have no part in anything which is less than 100 percent in accordance with the *halachah*.

I sometimes wonder if the consideration of a fee blurs the halachic sensitivity of the rare mohel who engages in these unauthorized practices. The mohel who performs milah for the mitzvah and not for an income will rarely find it difficult to decline the opportunity to circumcise a non-Jew. Perhaps it is somewhat unrealistic to expect all mohalim to work without a fee. Perhaps, alternatively, strict standards could be attained by close inspection and observation of all mohalim by a panel of *rabbonim*. However, considering the disorganized pattern of Jewish communal life, even within the Orthodox community, this is also a highly unlikely alternative.

There is one aspect of the problem which I have

just hinted at, an additional reason to be careful to determine the *yichus* (lineage) of the child to be circumcised—especially if a person's practice takes him frequently into non-observant Jewish homes. The state of American Jewish life is presently so confused that in a generation or two it may be very difficult for a large number of Jews to know, for certain, whether they are really Jews or not. Mixed marriages now constitute almost half of all Jewish marriages. The weaker a person's religious convictions, the greater the chance for marriage with a non-Jewish partner. When the mother of such a marriage is Jewish, all the children will be Jewish, but when the father is the Jewish partner, none of the children will be Jewish.

Of course, if the wife undergoes an authentic conversion before a properly constituted *Beis Din*, both she and her children born thereafter will be Jewish.* A person considering conversion must be very careful in seeking proper advice on the correct choice of a *Beis Din*, since the genuine article is hard to find, and there are many inauthentic substitutes around.

A mohel should carefully investigate the lineage of

---

*If the non-Jewish woman who wishes to become Jewish is pregnant, the *Beis Din* must be informed about her pregnancy so that they have in mind the conversion of the unborn child at the *t'vilah* (ritual immersion in the *mikvah*). Furthermore, if the unborn child is a boy, then the mohel, at the time of the bris, must have in mind that the circumcision is also for the purpose of *geirus* (conversion). The ceremony and the blessings, are, however, not changed.

all the children he is asked to circumcise, if for no other reason than that the child, should he ever have any doubts about whether or not he is genuinely Jewish, can rely on the fact that his mohel had the reputation for circumcising only children he had ascertained were of genuine stock.

A circumcision scene, beside the blessings recited by the mohel and the child's father: from MS Rothschild, an Ashkenazic miscellany from Italy, 1470, in the Israel Museum.

17

What's in a name?

A PLEA FOR JEWISH IDENTITY

As you go glancing through the local paper, your eye may light on something like this:

> United in marriage on Sunday, June 26, were Ianthe Heather Goldberg and Marlowe Sean Pearl. The ceremony took place at the Temple of Peace (formerly the Rodef Shalom Synagogue) in suburban Golus Heights, Long Island, with Rabbi Milton Bluestone officiating. Mrs. Pearl is a daughter of Mr. and Mrs. Morton Goldberger of Far Rockaway and a grand-daughter of Rev. and Mrs. Moshe Aaron Goldenberger of Crown Heights. The bridegroom's parents are Dr. and Mrs. Morris Pearlman of Scarsdale. His late grandparents were Rabbi and Mrs. Mendel Shraga Perlmutter of Williamsburg, Brooklyn. The bride is a graduate of Vassar and has published a book of poetry entitled *Affair with a Moonbeam*. The groom is a second-year student at Harvard Law School. The couple is residing in Cambridge, Massachusetts.

Reading the "Weddings—Engagements—Personals" page of any Anglo-Jewish newspaper in America reveals in a brief capsule the history of the Jewish community in this country. The adaptive modification of names from Aryeh Leib to Ernest Lawrence to Eric Lyman, or from Tzvi Hirsh to Stanley Howard to Sean Hadwin, accurately parallels the cultural decline of Jewish values during three generations of living in this land of opportunity. Indeed, we are quite relieved to see a Goldberg marrying a Pearl, a Roth wed to a Schwartz. Too often we come across a Cohn and a Crosby, a Levine and a McNulty. Of course, Crosby could have been a Crohn or Koenigsberg a generation or two ago, but I would be surprised if anyone in the last ten generations of McNulty ever set foot inside a *shul*.

Although we might be amused by this parade of names marching past us in the Jewish weeklies, we really have much cause for concern. The cultural assimilation which this procession of names represents does not make one optimistic about the survival of the Jewish people in America. It seems obvious to me that Jewish parents who are serious about Jewish cultural and ethnic survival, if nothing else, should give serious thought to the naming of their children. The Orthodox rabbinate has encouraged Jewish couples to have at least four or five children, the Reform at least two or three; but how will this contribute to a Jewish future if we unleash on the American scene a Rhea Sabina, John Cedric, Colbert Errol, Amity Holly, or Geoffrey Ewart? Will the future leaders of the Jewish people leap from these ranks?

My plea is: give your child a name of Jewish content, one that will remind him of his heritage, one that will protect him against a hostile environment. How much pride and history are implicit in a name like Moshe Aaron or Joshua David or Hadassah Esther or Ruth Naomi. Perhaps names such as these might provide that slight edge in a child's future struggle for cultural and biological survival.

Imagine my surprise when one of my fellow Jewish physicians named his newborn son Christopher. I asked him why he had chosen such an unusual name for a Jewish child, and wondered out loud if he knew what it meant. He told me, in complete innocence, that he and his wife liked the sound of the name, and, no, they were unaware of its meaning. He was being quite honest. He was completely ignorant of the subject (and, I might add, also very uninformed in the area of Jewish values and traditions).

It goes without saying that there are some personal names which any aware, knowing Jew would never give an offspring—such as Isabel (Jezebel—oath of Baal), Christine, or Christopher. Nor would his child be given the same name as any of the historical enemies of Israel, such as Adolf, Titus, or Haman. Yet we perform a similar, though not as extreme, disservice to our children if we name them after the inebriated and philandering crowned heads of Old England or Scotland, to wit: James, Edward, Harold, William, Richard, and the like. If we are enamoured of the name James, let us choose Jacob to which it is very distantly related.

Why the love affair with the Teutonic, the Celtic, the Latin? Do we think we are doing our children a favor by making it easier for them to assimilate? Why do we deprive ourselves of this first and great opportunity to direct our children to a Jewish frame of reference, to let our youngsters understand as they are growing up, how serious their parents were about having them grow up Jewish?

Of course, Jewish survival in a free country depends upon much more than a fortunate and wise choice of a name. Parents who are concerned about living a Jewish lifestyle both in and out of the home, schools which stress Jewish attitudes (yes, Jewish day schools), and a minimization of cultural intrusions which are alien to Jewish values (such as most television programming) are much more important factors in terms of Jewish survival.

But at the least let us make a good start. The traditional manner of naming a Jewish child has been to memorialize the memory of a departed relative, a grandparent, an aunt or an uncle. Boys are usually named after departed men, girls after women who have passed on. A Jewish child (at least in the Ashkenazic tradition) is never named after a living person and never after his father if the man is alive at the time of the child's birth. This is why we never see (or should never see) Yehuda Leib Jr., or Yehuda Leib III.

A boy is named at the time of his bris, at the age of

eight days. A girl is given a name within a week of her birth, at the synagogue, where a small party is usually tendered by the parents after the services. Your rabbi will be happy to assist you in choosing a proper name for your child, even if you have neglected to give him or her a Jewish name at birth. Even if the official "American" name of the birth certificate reads Gilbert Humphrey or Desiree Rowena, accustom the youngster to hear his Hebrew name at home. You may even want to consult your lawyer about changing the birth certificate name too.

Let us raise a Jewish generation of Jewish children. Then we may have a better chance of having some *yiddishe nachas* from them.

18

When there is no happiness

ONE OF THE SADDER DUTIES of a mohel involves the circumcision of an abortus, a stillborn, or a child who has died before the eighth day of life.

Jewish law is very clear regarding a child who has died before his circumcision: he is circumcised at the gravesite, in order to remove the foreskin, which is considered a disgrace for him. No blessings are uttered and there is no ceremony, but he is given a Jewish name appended to his father's name (so-and-so *ben*—the son of—so-and-so), to perpetuate his memory, so that mercy should be shown him from Heaven and he may thus be included in the Resurrection of the Dead, and so that he may have sufficient understanding to recognize his parents in the Time-to-Come (*Code of Jewish Law*).

Regarding such a child, Jewish law stipulates that if he was buried without being circumcised and people became aware of this omission immediately, before the body had sufficient time to decompose, the grave must be opened and the foreskin removed.

All the above applies to a child born live but who died before he had been circumcised.

Regarding an abortus, a fetus which has died in utero, or a stillborn child—an infant which has died just prior to birth, the custom is to circumcise such an infant also, though frequently this procedure will be done by the mohel in the funeral home.

I do not use my regular instruments at such a circumcision. I use a disposable surgical scalpel and a free-hand technique which involves no other equipment. The scalpel is discarded afterward. Only the foreskin is removed. There is no *priah*, and certainly no *metzitzah*. No *brochos* are recited, but the child is given a Jewish name.

One particularly macabre experience comes to mind. I was called by a member of the *Chevra Kadisha* of Cleveland, a voluntary organization of Jewish men and women whose function is to prepare the Jewish dead for burial. The preparation usually entails only washing the deceased in the funeral home and dressing him or her in *tachrichim*, the white shrouds in which Jews are buried. But frequently these volunteers become involved in other aspects of death and dying. This was one such instance.

A few days before, a seven-month fetus had died in its mother's womb and had to be removed piece by piece, through the dilated cervix of the uterus. The doctors at the hospital told the parents that it would have been a boy, but that because of the degree of decomposition and the trauma imposed by the method of removal, a ritual circumcision would not be possible. Nonetheless, the *Chevra Kadisha* called on me to examine the remains at the gravesite and to perform the ritual circumcision if at all possible.

That day remains sharp in my memory. It was snowing lightly. The weather was very cold and the roads were covered with ice. The cemetery was deserted except for one of the caretakers who had dug the shallow grave.

My two friends from the *Chevra Kadisha* and I were awaiting the rabbi from the synagogue with which the parents were affiliated. The parents were not here, nor was their presence required.

Then came the station wagon from the funeral home. The somber attendant parked next to us. Soon the rabbi arrived and we all got out of our cars.

The attendant was carrying a small wooden casket under his arm. Inside were the remains of the abortus which I would have to examine. I asked him to place the small casket in the back of the station wagon, so that I could open it and examine its contents to see if a circumcision would be possible.

I opened the casket, and was disturbed to find not an infant, but a plastic jar similar to an ice cream container. I put on a pair of plastic surgical gloves which I had brought with me and opened the container. My friends from the *Chevra Kadisha* and the rabbi turned pale and quickly backed off. I examined the contents of the jar carefully, bit by bit.

Yet try as I would, I could not find and identify the genitalia. There was nothing to do, so I returned everything to the jar and replaced it in the wooden casket. I also put the soiled gloves into the casket and closed the cover. The doctors were right. It would not be possible to perform a circumcision.

We walked slowly to the open grave, the rabbi, my two friends from the *Chevra Kadisha*, the attendant from the funeral home and myself. He had just dug a shallow grave. The tiny casket was lowered into it. The rabbi said a short prayer of *El moley rachamim* ("O Lord, full of mercy...") giving the unborn fetus a Jewish name. We took turns shoveling the damp cold earth into the grave, in accordance with the ancient Jewish custom.

I can only thank Providence that such an experience is very rare, and hardly ever repeated.

19

Summing up

THE JEWISH COMMUNITY should be vitally interested in strengthening the practice of bris milah. As I have tried to bring out in this short book, milah is not simply a cosmetic surgical procedure, but a major integral part of the cultural heritage of an ancient people. It is a central element of Jewish life, that contributes greatly to the continued survival of the Jewish nation, and it is observed to one degree or another by everyone who considers himself Jewish.

The greatest obstacle to the universal practice of traditional bris milah is the lack of knowledge about this mitzvah. All Jewish parents want their sons to be circumcised, but how many know enough to distinguish between mere circumcision and a properly performed bris milah? A circumcision performed in the hospital by a physician or a medical student is not a bris milah. Yet how many Jews know this?

Part of the blame can be placed at the door of the

traditional Jewish community, for we know about this mitzvah and yet have really given it very little public attention. Alongside our efforts to enlighten the general Jewish community about the importance of *kashrus*, Shabbos, and Jewish day-school education, we should also endeavor to disseminate information about bris milah.

Those who have read this book can now consider themselves learned at least in the basics of this mitzvah, and now carry an obligation to enlighten their fellow Jews. This is indeed consistent with the general Jewish attitude about education — that every Jew has the responsibility to teach his neighbor who may know less than he. Therefore, if a Jew knows only the *aleph beis*, he should teach it to a Jew who does not know even this.

Parenthetically, I would like to stress that the Jewish mother herself can bring about great changes in the community and in her own personal life by informing her obstetrician and pediatrician that she wants a ritual circumcision to be performed on her own offspring on his eighth day. She and her husband should consult a qualified mohel as soon as their son is born. If the mother must remain in the hospital for more than a week, the parents must insist that the mohel be permitted to do the milah in the traditional fashion in the hospital.

This decision on the part of the parents will send ripples of interest throughout the community, and the result will be that before long, knowledge of this mitzvah will become widespread.

There are other ways in which this information can achieve greater attention. For example, here is a letter which might be sent by the Board of Rabbis, or by a traditionally minded physician, or by an interested and motivated housewife, to all the physicians in town, both Jewish and non-Jewish:

Dear Dr.———:

I am sending this letter to you and other pediatricians and obstetricians in Cleveland to publicize some important aspects of a subject of vital interest to their Jewish patients—namely, ritual circumcision (bris milah).

From the very beginning of Jewish history, ritual circumcision has been the practice of the Jewish people. No matter how great the persecution or how complete the assimilation into a foreign culture, the Jewish nation has never forsaken the "sign of the covenant," which has always been an essential element of our heritage. No matter what a Jew has given up—his kosher food, his Sabbath observance, his synagogue affiliation—he has always insisted that his sons be circumcised.

I would like to stress that there are important differences between a circumcision and a bris milah (ritual circumcision):

1. The ritual circumcision must be performed no earlier than the eighth day of life.
2. The technique of ritual circumcision does differ in certain important details from a standard surgical circumcision.
3. Bris milah should be performed by a

> mohel, a man who has been especially trained and certified in the techniques, laws and customs of the ritual circumcision.
>
> I earnestly implore you to suggest to your Jewish patients that they give their new son a proper bris milah. I am enclosing some literature on the subject which has been prepared by the Mount Sinai Hospital for new Jewish mothers.
>
> *Sincerely,* etc.

I would be happy to send interested readers a sample of this leaflet of the Mount Sinai Hospital (of Cleveland; illustrated on p. 156), or you may obtain it directly by writing to the hospital, thus:

Mr. Barry Spero, Director,
Mount Sinai Hospital of Cleveland,
University Circle, Cleveland, Ohio 44106

Of course, if the rabbis in our communities would occasionally devote a few minutes of their sermons or a few lines in the congregational newsletter to the subject of bris milah, enormous gains could be realized. You might speak to your rabbi about this. You will be surprised to see what he can do.

Nor should the mohalim be content merely to wait passively to be called on by interested parents. To be a mohel, indeed to occupy any position of Jewish content in the community, carries with it a responsibility to teach and to publicize correct Jewish practice. A mohel should not hide behind the mantle of false modesty, saying to himself that he cannot

RITUAL
CIRCUMCISION — BRITH MILAH

We are happy to assist parents in arranging a ritual circumcision at the hospital. These religious ceremonies are held in the Prayer Room on the first floor of Building B. Your son's Hebrew name will be conferred as part of the Brith Milah ritual.

We will take care of some of the arrangements and will depend upon you to take care of others. This is what we ask you to do.

1. First check with your doctor to determine that your baby is in good health for the ritual circumcision and to find out when he will be discharged from the hospital. Then contact the Mohel and let him decide, according to the date and time of the baby's birth, on what day the ritual circumcision will be performed. Only the following Mohelim are permitted to perform ritual circumcision at Mt. Sinai Hospital:
   Rabbi Schlomo Davis
   Dr. Henry Romberg
   Rabbi Daniel Schur
2. After you have made arrangements with your Mohel, inform the Division Secretary. She will make reservations for the Prayer Room (usually the ceremony is scheduled for 10:30 a.m.; however, it may be later if there are others scheduled on the same day). You will be asked to sign a release permit.
3. Please note that you are asked not to invite more than 16 persons to participate in the ceremony. This limitation is for the protection of your baby.
4. Members of your family will be expected provide refreshments (wine and sponge ca or honey cake are traditional) as well glasses or paper cups, a table cloth, a t for the cake, and a knife.

We will provide a surgical tray containing t necessary circumcision equipment prepared the Central Sterile Supply Room; we will assi a nurse to take your baby to the Prayer Roo and to remain with him throughout the ce mony; we will prepare the Prayer Room for t ceremony.

Following the services the baby will be tak to his mother s room to be prepared for d charge from the hospital.

If you have any questions about these matte the Division Secretary will be pleased to ass you.

NOTE:

It should be noted that a Brith Milah **nev** occurs before the eighth day after birth. If t Brith Milah does **not** take place at the hospit please contact the Mohel directly to make the necessary arrangements.

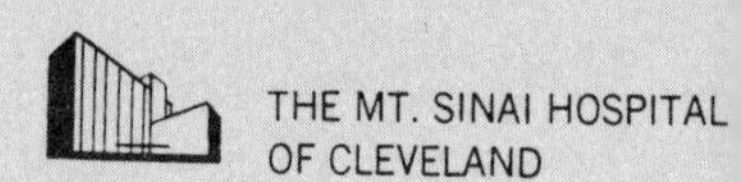

A leaflet given to mothers of newborn infants in the Mt. Sinai Hosptial of Cleveland who want information about ritual circumcision.

speak publicly because that would seem like soliciting business for himself.

Sadly, too, many of us are caught up in the incorrect belief that the performance of milah is some sort of commercial enterprise. Our business is promoting the sacred mitzvah of bris milah. This is a mitzvah which, as our Sages have informed us, sustains the world in its very existence. And we are worried about seeming to be self-serving? If you are so concerned about appearing to solicit business for yourself, simply donate all your fees to charity. Then you will have no self-recriminations about the matter. And you will have the extra mitzvah of *tzedakah* (Jewish charity) to boot!

Similarly, the *sofer* (scribe) of a community, the bookseller, the *mikvah* association, the Board of Kashrus and the kosher food outlets, and the congregational rabbis should promote their wares. No one accuses the medical profession of unprofessional conduct or of self interest when we warn people to take care of their health. Let the entire Jewish community benefit from your services. Let the entire community hear from you—again and again—until the message gets through.

Some mohalim have published brochures or booklets for the parents of the infant.

It is my hope that this book will serve not only as an aid to new parents but as a means to publicize the mitzvah of bris milah and to educate the English-speaking Jewish community in this far-too-often neglected subject.

FAMILY NAME (English) ....

....(Hebrew) שם המשפחה

CHILD'S GIVEN NAME ....

.... שם התינוק

FATHER'S NAME ....

.... שם האב

MOTHER'S NAME ....

.... שם האם

DATE OF BIRTH .... תאריך הלידה

DATE OF BRIS .... יום הברית

PLACE OF BRIS .... מקום הברית

SANDEK .... הסנדק

GODFATHER .... הקוואַטער

GODMOTHER .... הקוואַטערין

PARENTS' ADDRESS .... כתובת ההורים

....

TELEPHONE .... מספר הטלפון

MOHEL'S NAME .... שם המוהל

SIGNATURE .... חתימתו

An example of a certificate that a mohel can give the parents of a child, to attest to his entry into the Covenant of Abraham

Appendices

By now, I am sure you will have some idea of the basic laws, traditions, and practices which apply to the subject of this book. In the following pages, I have summarized many of these points in an orderly fashion, for more convenient reference. The very last appendix includes "Questions and Answers" which (as I know from experience) will be of interest to parents who are having a bris.

The basic source for most of the laws of bris milah, indeed, the source of most of the laws and traditions that apply to the everyday life of the observant Jew, is the great compendium of Jewish law, the *Shulchan Aruch*, with its classic commentaries.

This great Code of Law, the *Shulchan Aruch* ("The Arranged Table"), is the work of Rabbi Joseph Karo (1488-1575), who set down in it legal decisions relevant to every aspect of Jewish life. He based his decisions on the discussions of the Talmud and the decisions of the outstanding legalists who preceded him. The greatest minds of the Jewish people have continually worked over these decisions, showing how they may be applied in the different countries of our exile and rendering them relevant to changing times and cultures in which Jewish people find themselves. The genius of Jewish law is that its source is Divine, and it is therefore totally relevant to all times and to all places. Consequently, it is no surprise to find discussions in the rabbinic literature on such diverse subjects as the order of prayer in the synagogue, the use of electricity on the Shabbos, or the proper time for the observance of Shabbos in outer space!

Matters of Jewish law are not arbitrarily decided but are studied with painstaking care and immense detail before any decision is rendered. It is simply inconceivable to change the basic principle upon which the law is based, or to "re-interpret" the law to arrive at a decision more in line with "the spirit of the times." The sages of each generation have the task of finding what the Torah has to say about any new technology or any situation which may arise, and deciding how to treat it *within* the great framework of the *halachah*.

APPENDIX I

LAWS OF BRIS MILAH

1. It is a positive Torah commandment for a father to circumcise his sons. It is the most important of all positive commandments applicable today.

2. The time of milah is the eighth day, even if the eighth day falls on a Shabbos, or even if it falls on Yom Kippur. People are generally careful to do this mitzvah early in the day, even if the bris had been postponed for medical reasons. Early or late, however, it must be done during the day, never at night.

3. We do not circumcise an ill infant, whether he is determined to be ill by a pediatrician or by the criteria established by Jewish tradition. In a systemic illness (one affecting the entire body), he is circumcised seven full days after he has completely recovered.

Infections or inflammations of the eye are counted as systemic illnesses. *Physiologic jaundice of the newborn* is considered a "malady affecting only one limb" (and therefore not a "systemic illness"). Other types of jaundice, however, are treated as systemic illnesses and cause the bris to be postponed until the end of a full week from the time of recovery.

4. A malady affecting one limb requires the bris to be postponed until that illness has been completely overcome, and then the bris is done immediately. A postponed bris is not done at night, nor is it done on Shabbos or Yom Tov, but rather during a regular day.

5. A child born via Cesarian section is not circum-

cised on the eighth day if that day happens to be Shabbos or Yom Tov.

6. The laws concerning the bris milah of a child born at dusk, between sunset and the appearance of the stars, are complex, and it is therefore important to consult a competent Orthodox scholar in this case. If you have to call the rabbi by telephone, you should know the exact time the baby was born (when his head emerged from the birth canal; if you see that there is going to be a problem with the time, ask your obstetrician to note this time for you), and also the official time for sunset in your city.

7. Certain discolorations of the child's skin will compel the mohel to postpone the bris, even if the pediatrician insists that it is perfectly safe to perform the operation. The mohel has no choice. The Law compels him to postpone the bris. You will save him considerable embarrassment if you do not try to argue with him on this matter. On the other hand, even if all the criteria for the performance of a bris are met, yet the pediatrician suggests that the bris be postponed for a medical reason, here too, the mohel will postpone the bris.

I will not go into the details of criteria about the color of the baby's skin, since this is a matter of experience on the part of the mohel and cannot be conveyed by words alone. The *Shulchan Aruch* concludes its section on illnesses which cause the postponement of a bris by stating the general principle governing the entire matter: we do not circumcise a newborn if there is a doubt as to his good health, because danger to life pushes aside all other considerations. It is possible to circumcise him at a later time but it is not possible to restore even a single Jewish soul (if the child should die).

8. Jewish tradition recognized long ago the genetic transmission of certain clotting disorders which might result in fatal hemorrhage if circumcision were to be performed in infancy. The details of this legislation are found in the Talmud, first recorded 1500 years ago in Babylon. If this bleeding disorder is found in a woman's children, subsequent children are not circumcised until they grow older and can better withstand the procedure. If two sisters have such children with bleeding tendencies, the children of a third sister are not circumcised until they grow older.

9. An infant who has died before the eighth day is circumcised at the gravesite, but without a *brocho*. He is given a Jewish name, so that Heaven will show mercy to him and he shall arise at the Resurrection of the Dead.

10. It is forbidden to circumcise a gentile, except for medical reasons or for the purpose of conversion.

11. The mohel must be an observant Jew.

12. There are many circumstances where it is our custom to perform *hatofas dam bris*. The mohel causes a small amount of bleeding with a pin prick at the glans or the shaft of the penis just behind the glans. (There are two opinions concerning where to withdraw the blood. I hold the first opinion, on the authority of Rabbi Moshe Bick.) I prick the skin with a sterile 18-gauge hypodermic needle until a tiny drop of blood appears. This is the *dam bris*, the blood of the Covenant, and corrects any ritual defect which may have existed in the past. Competent rabbinic opinion should be sought in this matter, since a blessing may be required if the *hatofas dam bris* is obligatory, whereas no *brocho* is made if the *kashrus* (validity) of the original milah is only *in doubt*. The *brocho* would be "Blessed are You . . . Who has sanctified us with His commandments and commanded us to withdraw the blood of the Covenant."

13. Once parents have engaged a particular mohel, they should not change to another mohel. If, however, they subsequently find out that the first mohel does not do milah properly, they may choose another.

14. A mohel who does not do *metzitzah b'peh* either in the traditional manner or, according to some, with a glass tube, is not performing bris milah properly and his services should be avoided.

15. During the bris, the father stands next to the mohel, to make it evident that the mohel is performing the circumcision on behalf of the father (as his deputy). The mitzvah is the father's, and it is only because of his inexperience that he has given over the task to an expert. If the father is a mohel, he should circumcise his own son.

16. The custom is to have a feast after the bris milah,

with a *minyan* of at least ten men in attendance if possible. This is referred to as a *se'udas mitzvah* (festive meal in honor of a commandment). If the bris falls on a fast day, the cup of wine over which the blessings are said at the bris is given to a child to drink (except on Yom Kippur). Then the *se'udas mitzvah* is held in the evening. Of the six fast days (Yom Kippur, Tisha B'Av, Tsom Gedaliah, Asarah B'Teiveis, Shiva Asar B'Tammuz, and Ta'anis Esther) only the fast of Ta'anis Esther is lifted because of the happiness of the bris milah. On Ta'anis Esther the *sandek*, the mohel, and the infant's parents are allowed to break their fast in the afternoon. However, the bris is held in the morning as usual (*Chofetz Chaim*).

17. In the week before Tisha B'Av, a mohel may trim his fingernails in preparation for the performance of the bris. Similarly, meat and wine may be served during the Nine Days before Tisha B'Av at the *se'udah* following the bris, but not on the afternoon of the day before the fast. During these days, the mohel, the *sandek*, the father, and the *kvatterin* may don their Shabbos clothes. These may also have their hair cut in honor of the bris, but not after *Shabbos Chazon* (the last Shabbos before the fast of Tisha B'Av) (*Kitzur Shulchan Aruch*).

18. If the bris falls on Tisha B'Av, the *sandek*, mohel, and parents of the child may wear their fine Shabbos clothes (but not leather shoes), but after the circumcision they should remove these clothes and wear the garb customary for this day of mourning. The bris should take place after the recital of *kinnos*. The glass of wine is given to a minor to drink. If Tisha B'Av falls on Shabbos and the fast is therefore postponed to Sunday (since fasting is not allowed on Shabbos, except for Yom Kippur), the *sandek*, mohel, and parents of the infant may break their fast in the afternoon, but the *se'udah* should not be held until nightfall.

19. Even though the performance of the milah itself involves several types of activity which would otherwise be prohibited on Shabbos, nevertheless a bris milah is done on Shabbos or Yom Tov if that is the eighth day of the child's life. However, all the preparations for the bris, such as bringing instruments to the house, preparing the dressings, and so forth, must be done before Shabbos. For this reason, the mohel will leave his instruments at the house Friday and walk back on Shabbos to perform the bris.

20. During *Sefirah*, the seven weeks of limited mourning between Passover and Shavuos, when Jews do not listen to secular music, engage in public celebration, or cut their hair, the *sandek*, the mohel, and the father of the infant are allowed to have their hair cut in the afternoon before the bris. A *se'udas mitzvah* is also permitted.

21. If a circumcision is to be performed in *shul* on Purim morning, it is done before the *Megillah* is read (*Kitzur Shulchan Aruch*).

APPENDIX II

SOME LAWS ON MARRIAGE, CONVERSION, AND DIVORCE

Every problem is different, and should be brought to an Orthodox rabbi who is *competent* to discuss and advise on such matters (and many fine Orthodox rabbis will admit that they do not consider themselves competent to render decisions in certain areas of the Law). The following is a general outline which will, at the least, alert the reader when to ask a question.

Marriage Laws

1. It is absolutely forbidden for a Jew to marry a gentile. Such a "marriage" not only has no legal standing in the eyes of the Law, but is considered a grave sin for the Jewish partner.

2. Children born of such a mixed marriage follow the mother in terms of peoplehood. If the mother is Jewish, they are Jewish. If the father is Jewish, the children are not Jewish.

3. The non-Jewish partner of a mixed marriage can be converted to Judaism if he or she is totally willing to accept an observant Jewish way of life. This includes Shabbos observance, *kashrus*, and the laws and practices of *mikvah*. Conversion is not merely a ritual done *to* a potential convert; it requires the wholehearted desire and involvement of the convert. Non-Jewish children of such a marriage may also be converted while still infants or children, but they have the option of reverting to their non-Jewish status when they come of age (twelve years for a girl, thirteen for a boy).

4. Conversions must be done according to the *halachah*, the body of Jewish law as practiced and understood by a competent Orthodox court. Reform and other non-Orthodox conversions are worthless. Not only are they not recognized throughout the world or in the State of Israel but, more importantly, they are not recognized in Heaven.

5. A Jew, no matter how far he or she has strayed from his people, is still considered 100% Jewish even though that person is not *acting Jewishly*. He may not be a *good* Jew, but a Jew he is until the day he leaves this world. A non-Jew may convert to Judaism, but a Jew can never leave his Jewish status, even though he has adopted another religion or lifestyle.

Divorce Laws

1. If a couple dissolves their marriage without a Jewish divorce (*get*) provided by a competent Orthodox *Beis Din*, they remain married in the eyes of the Law and subsequent remarriage would be considered adulterous and therefore an illegal union.

2. If a Jewish woman who was married to a Jew remarries without a *get*, her new relationship is considered to be adulterous and her subsequent offspring, if her new mate is Jewish, are *mamzerim* (illegitimate) and forever forbidden to marry within the Jewish fold.

3. If a man remarries but has not previously dissolved the marriage with his first (Jewish) wife with a *get*, his subsequent union is considered polygamous and is outlawed by rabbinical law.

4. If both husband and wife wish to divorce each other, a *get* is very easy to obtain. A Jewish court can issue a *get* in an afternoon, and the cost will never be a problem.

5. A man cannot unilaterally divorce his wife, nor can a wife unilaterally divorce her husband.

6. Of course, no religious divorce is needed if one of the marital partners is non-Jewish.

7. Realizing the problems which may befall a couple if they do not get a proper *get*, many Reform and Conservative rabbis as well as a number of lawyers involved in divorce proceedings recommend that the couple go to an Orthodox *Beis Din* for their *get*. For this they are to be highly praised and will receive their reward from the Divine Source of true reward.

8. Any Jewish woman, even if she is not in the least interested in religion or ritual, should make a *get* part of her divorce settlement. She can never know what the future will hold. Perhaps she will want to remarry. Her new husband may not want to marry without her obtaining a *get* from her first husband. She may subsequently have children by another husband, and without a *get*, these children will have a difficult time finding mates in all but the most irreligious circles. They (and all their descendants) will be *mamzerim*.

APPENDIX III

QUESTIONS I HAVE BEEN ASKED

The Baby

Q. My child has Down's Syndrome (Mongolism). Will that postpone the bris?

A. If he is otherwise healthy, the bris must take place on the eighth day after birth.

Q. Should I feed the baby before the bris?

A. Ask your mohel what his preference is. My own inclination is to feed him whenever he is hungry, even if this is just before the bris. If he is not fed, he will cry during the entire ceremony, both before and after the milah.

Q. Can I put the baby down on his stomach after the bris?

A. I prefer to position a newly-circumcised child on his side or back for 24-36 hours afterwards, to minimize irritation to the operative site. However, if a newborn is going to be placed on his back, I like to elevate the head of the crib three or four inches.

Q. How should I dress the baby for the bris?

A. You may dress him in anything the bottom half of which is easily removed. Have a few extra diapers ready for the mohel to use if the baby should wet or soil his clothes. Sometimes the parents send the baby in with a small *yarmulka* (*kippah*) or skullcap on his head. This will fall off unless you secure it to the scalp with a little adhesive tape.

Q. It is now two weeks after the bris and there is still some swelling behind the top of the penis. What is wrong?

A. There is nothing wrong. What you are seeing is edema (swelling) of the mucosal layer of the prepuce which now forms part of the penile shaft skin. Occasionally, this delicate tissue will swell for a few weeks. Warm soaks will speed its return to a normal appearance.

Q. Our town has no mohel and we will have to fly one in from Chicago. What shall I do if the baby starts to bleed after the mohel leaves?

A. First, call him up on the phone and ask his advice. What you think is bleeding may only be urine which has soaked up some blood from the bandaging.

If there is really significant bleeding or if you cannot get in touch with the mohel, call your pediatrician. The problem with calling a physician, however, is that the only way most doctors know to stop bleeding is to suture, when all that may be required is a new application of the circular gauze dressing.

I would be pleased to talk with any physician about any questions he may have concerning ritual circumcision.

Q. I've heard that I should not take aspirin if I'm breast-feeding. Why?

A. The aspirin will be passed to your baby via your milk. This may delay hemostasis (the ability of an open wound to stop bleeding), since aspirin has a slight anti-clotting effect on the blood. Your mohel will probably instruct you not to take any aspirin or aspirin-containing compounds (like Empirin or

Bufferin) for 48 hours before and 24 hours after the bris.

The Mohel

Q. How much does a mohel charge for his services?

A. No mohel "charges" for doing a mitzvah. Mohalim, however, do appreciate a gratuity, the size of which varies with the geographic location or the special circumstances of the bris. I'm told that the average gratuity in New York is about $75-$100.

Of course, if you must have the mohel fly in from another city or state, you would have to pay for his air fare and related expenses.

Many mohalim donate part or all of their income from milah to *tzedakah* (charity).

Q. What does the mohel do with the severed skin?

A. At the bris, it is placed in a receptacle filled with earth. Afterwards, the mohel will bury it. I bury all in my backyard.

Q. Our Young Marrieds group would like to know more about bris milah. Can you recommend any additional reading material?

A. There is very little in English which discusses ritual circumcision properly at length. The encyclopedias, both Jewish and secular, present a distorted and rather non-Jewish view of this subject. Volume II of the English translation of the *Yalkut Me-Am Lo'ez* (pages 122-143) as well as Julius Preuss' *Biblical and Talmudic Medicine* (pages 240-248) both contain excellent discussions of milah.

I would suggest that you invite the mohalim in your community to address your group.

Q. Our city's mohel has just retired and moved out of state. How do we go about finding another one?

A. Very few mohalim can make a living from milah. However, if some other position should become available in your community (such as rabbi, *shammash*, day school teacher, and so forth), let it be known that you would prefer to hire someone who is also a qualified mohel. Until you are able to procure such a person, you will have to have a mohel come in from another city.

Q. The only mohel in our town is not *Shomer Shabbos* (Sabbath-observing Jew). What should we do?

A. This mohel must not be used. Until you can get an observant Jewish mohel, you will have to use a mohel from another city.

Q. Dr. Romberg, after reading your book, I wonder if someone interested in becoming a mohel could learn enough from these pages to start practicing milah?

A. Can one become a rabbi from book-learning alone? Can one learn to be a doctor from a book? Only a very foolish person indeed would attempt to practice milah with only book learning to his credit. This book has not been intended to serve as background reading for prospective mohalim. The interested student must study the original Hebrew sources and apprentice himself to a competent mohel.

Q. I am presently in the *kollel* (graduate studies department) of a yeshivah on the East Coast and would like to learn to become a mohel. How do I get started?

A. Study everything you can get your hands on about milah. There is a wealth of material in Hebrew. Then ask the advice, permission, and blessing of your Rebbe or *rosh yeshivah*. Finally, apprentice yourself to an experienced mohel and spend as much time with him as you can. You will probably perform your first bris on your own son.

The Ceremony

Q. Why is it considered such an honor to be asked to be the *sandek* at a bris?

A. The *sandek* is the one who holds the baby during the actual circumcision. In many ways the office of *sandek* is more important than that of mohel: If the Torah is being read in the synagogue on the morning of the bris the *sandek* is called up *before* the mohel. Our sages regard the knees of the *sandek*, upon which the baby rests, as the altar of the Holy Temple, and his holding the child as tantamount to offering incense upon the golden altar in the Holy Chamber.

The reward for being the *sandek* at a bris is wealth, which we understand to mean Torah knowledge, the only true wealth.

Q. Why is there a Chair of Elijah (*Kisei shel Eliyahu*) at a bris?

A. We have a tradition that God commanded Elijah the Prophet to be present at every circumcision, as a reproof for his accusation that "...the Children of Israel have forsaken Your covenant" (I Kings 19:10). Elijah is invited in the ritual to every bris, to observe how faithfully the Jewish people have clung to this precious mitzvah even in periods of history when they have been lax about other traditional observances.

Q. When is the best time of day for a bris?

A. A mitzvah should be performed at the earliest possible opportunity. Since the arrival of the eighth day permits us to perform this precept, we try to do the bris early in the day, as soon after sunrise as possible. It is customary for the men to *daven* (say the morning prayers) before the bris, and the ritual circumcision occurs right afterwards. Of course, if the mohel has another bris to perform or if he has to travel some distance to the home of the baby, this might require postponing the ceremony for a few hours. Nonetheless, the general principle is: as early as possible—even for a bris which has been postponed past the eighth day for health reasons.

1

1. The mohel says a prayer before the circumcision.

2. The child is brought in.

3. The circumcision is performed.

2

Illustrations in a manuscript copy o R. David Lida's So **haShem,** ***the laws and text of the cir cumcision ritual, with a kabbalisti commentary (written and draw in Amsterdam, 177***

3

4

4. *While the child is held, the subsequent blessings are recited over a cup of wine.*

5. *Birkas ha-mazon (Grace) is recited at the se'udas mitzvah, the meal that traditionally follows the bris. At the left is the infant's mother, with a woman in attendance.*

6. *After the bris: The child is apparently being bathed by the mohel before it is put in swaddling clothes and given back to the mother.*

5

6

SUPPLEMENT

The Significance of the Covenant

a chapter from *Ish uBeitho* by

Eliyahu Kitov

translated from the Hebrew by Chava Shulman

"Now when Avram was ninety-nine years old, HA-SHEM revealed Himself to Avram and said to him, 'I am the Almighty God of providence; walk before Me and be perfect. And I shall establish my covenant between Me and you, and will multiply you exceedingly.' Then Avram fell upon his face, and God spoke with him, saying, 'As for Me, here is My covenant with you, and you shall be the father of a multitude of nations. And you will no longer be called Avram, but your name will be Avraham, for I have made you the father of a multitude of nations. And I shall make you exceedingly fruitful and will make you into nations, and kings will descend from you. And I will maintain My covenant between Me and you and your progeny after you throughout their generations as an everlasting covenant—to be God to you and to your descendants after you. And I will give you and your descendants after you the land of your sojourning—the entire land of Canaan—as an everlasting possession, and I shall be God to them.' Then God said to Avraham, 'On your part, you shall observe My covenant, you and your progeny after you throughout their generations. This is My covenant, which you shall keep, between Me and all your progeny after you: every male among you shall be circumcised. And you are to circumcise the flesh of your foreskins, and this will be a sign of the covenant between Me and you. Now, at the age of eight days shall every male among you be circumcised, throughout your generations, [including] anyone born in the household or anyone purchased for money, any gentile who is not descended from you. Anyone born in your household or purchased with your money is to be circumcised, and My covenant in your flesh will be an everlasting covenant. And an uncircumcised male who will not have his foreskin circumcised—that person will be cut off from his people; he has broken My covenant' " (Genesis 17:1-15).

"And God said: Nevertheless, your wife Sarah will bear

you a son, and you will call him Yitzchak; and I will establish My covenant with him as a permanent covenant, and with his descendants after him" (*ibid.* 19).

"And I will establish My covenant with Yitzchak, whom Sarah will bear to you at this time next year" (*ibid.* 21).

THE SECRET OF ISRAEL'S MERIT

Why did HA-SHEM wait to give the mitzvah of circumcision to Avraham (and to no one before him)? The Torah says, "The *secret* counsel of the Lord is with those that fear Him; it is His covenant to let them recognize it" (Psalms 25).

What is this *secret* of the Lord?

It is the mitzvah of circumcision which was revealed to Avraham only after twenty generations had passed from the time of Adam. God said to Avraham: If you will circumcise yourself, you will share this *secret* and benefit from it.

The numerical value of the letters in *sod*, the Hebrew word for *secret*, is seventy (*samech* = 60, *vav* = 6, *daled* = 4; together, 70). Thus HA-SHEM said: I will establish seventy souls from you through the merit of circumcision . . . and I shall establish from them seventy elders . . . and from them I will bring Moshe into existence, who will study the Torah in seventy tongues—through the merit of circumcision (Yalkut Shimoni on Psalms, 702).

Another passage in the Midrash makes the same point:

In reward for performing the mitzvah of milah, and for their loyalty to this covenant, greatness was to be bestowed upon Avraham and his descendants. By observing the *secret* of the Lord, they would merit to have the *seventy* souls who descended to Egypt be increased to 600,000—the people of HA-SHEM—at the time of their deliverance from Egypt. Seventy elders were to bear the burden of a whole people and transform a mass of slaves into a kingdom of *kohanim* (Divine servants) and a holy people. Our teacher

Moshe was to interpret the Torah in seventy languages and instruct his nation how to disseminate its teaching among seventy nations, until the world would be filled with the knowledge of HA-SHEM at the end of days.

[Milah, sacred circumcision, is the sign of a covenant with God which gave the Jewish people both the opportunity and the responsibility to achieve greatness. It is of interest to note that the reward for milah is not an end in itself, such as land or wealth; rather, Jewry receives the ability to achieve greatness through its own efforts, in a dynamic historical process, as attested by the relation between this mitzvah and the number seventy—seventy elders who will transform slaves to Divine servants, seventy languages in which to teach. The number seventy is connected with Jewry's means for continually actualizing its mission.]*

Now why did HA-SHEM wait until Avraham was ninety-nine? Why did He not have him undergo circumcision decades earlier, when he recognized and accepted God? The Almighty's purpose was to leave converts no excuse [to argue that they are too old].

Again, why did He not have Avraham undergo circumcision at seventy-five, when HA-SHEM spoke to him at the Covenant of the Pieces (*brith bein ha-betharim*)? His purpose was that Yitzchak (alone) should be conceived from the first pure issue (*ibid.* 80).

I AM EL SHADDAI

When Avraham was given the commandment of milah, God manifested Himself to him with the words "*I am El Shaddai*" (Genesis 17:1). As Rashi interprets this, it means: I am He who has *sufficient* Godliness for every creature; therefore, "walk before Me." [The word *shaddai* can also be read as *she-dai* 'that which is sufficient, enough.']

---

* Translator's note.

A person who serves HA-SHEM without first entering into a covenant with Him, may possibly be serving only himself, because he finds God's nearness pleasant. This person can easily fall prey to feelings of envy, as he will be afraid that if others draw close to Him they will detract from his own nearness to the Divine (as if God's powers were not sufficient for all). He will furthermore worship only as long as he derives benefit from it, since there is no covenant to bind him unconditionally.

On the other hand, when a person serves HA-SHEM because he is bound by an indelible covenant sealed in the flesh, he will understand that God must be served for His sake alone. He will neither forsake his belief nor envy others theirs. On the contrary, just as God desires to draw all men close to Himself, so will the *ben brith* (son of the covenant) desire this. Thus HA-SHEM told Avraham, "Walk before Me": show yourself to everyone, to make God's presence known—for He has enough Godliness for all; He is *Shaddai—sufficient* for all.

With these words, "I am *El Shaddai*," God as much as said to Avraham: From the time of creation I waited twenty generations for you to come and accept the mitzvah of milah. If you do not accept it now, I shall revert the world back to chaos, as I have no further need for it. Therefore did God manifest Himself now to Avraham with His name *Shaddai*—to imply: the world has existed long *enough* (i.e. *dai*, sufficient). Should you accept this mitzvah, however, the merit of our covenant shall alone be *enough* (*dai*) to sustain the world! (Yalkut Shimoni, I 247, 80)

The Almighty has no desire for a world which accepts or rejects Him at whim; there must be some persons sworn to Him eternally by bearing the mark of a covenant. Even if they themselves should deny its implications, others will recognize it and assert: *You* are surely the servants of HA-SHEM! And even if they be few in number, their merit is *enough* (*dai*) to sustain the world.

WITHOUT BLEMISH

"I am the Almighty God of providence; walk before Me and be *tamim*, perfect [without blemish]" (Genesis 17:1).

Said Rabbi Yehudah haNasi: See how great the mitzvah of milah is! There was no one so concerned with the practice of mitzvoth as our father Avraham, yet he was not called *tamim*, perfect, until he underwent milah, as it is written, "Walk before Me and be *tamim* (perfect)."

A person may perform all the mitzvoth and yet not be deemed complete (perfected) until he has observed this mitzvah. "As the first fruit on the fig tree in its first season, I saw your fathers" (Hosea 9:10). Rabbi Yudan explained: Just as a fig has no waste matter except its stem—remove it and the blemish is gone—so did the Holy One say to Avraham: You have no imperfection but the *orlah* (foreskin). Remove it and the imperfection is gone; "walk before Me and be perfect" (Bereshith Rabbah 46:1).

Rami bar Abba said: At first he was called Avram (whose Hebrew letters have a numerical value of 243), and this was changed to Avraham (whose numerical value in Hebrew letters is 248, the total number of limbs and organs of the body). At first Avraham was in control of only 243 of his organs and limbs—and after circumcision, he gained mastery over the remaining five, including the eyes, ears and organ of procreation (Nedarim 32).

Until his brith, Avraham controlled all his organs in the service of the Creator except for his senses of vision and hearing, and sexual proclivity—for a person ordinarily has little control over these senses and desires. Following his milah, however, when he alone among all living beings became sanctified to God, he could assume mastery over *all* his senses and sensual faculties; that he might neither see nor hear nor desire anything but that which was acceptable to God.

Therefore is it written, "and be perfect": in perfect

control over all your organs—as reflected in Avraham's change of name.

STRENGTH TO ITS ADHERENTS

"And Avraham fell upon his face . . ." (Genesis 17:3) —until his circumcision, Avraham was unable to stand in the presence of God, but afterwards, he was able to remain on his feet when the Almighty appeared—as it is written, "And Avraham remained standing before HA-SHEM" (Genesis 18:22).

Moreover, God revealed Himself to him even when Avraham was seated, as it is written, "And HA-SHEM revealed Himself to him by the plain of Mamre as he sat at the entrance to his tent" (Genesis 18:1; Midrash Tanchuma on *Bereshith*, 20).

Paradoxically, initial submission is a prerequisite for ultimate strength.

Before his milah, Avraham could not be wholly subservient to God, as his sight, hearing and procreative faculty were yet independent forces. When the Almighty appeared to him in this state, Avraham's submissive soul possessed the ability to stand in the Divine Presence, but not his body—and it fell.

Following milah, however, Avraham assumed mastery over the totality of his senses. He was now able to remain standing, as his entire being was infused with the strength that follows total dedication.

Not only the individual, but the entire people of Israel and Jewry gain strength in an hour of war against their enemies, by the merit of milah: "For HA-SHEM your God walks in the midst of your camp to give your enemies up before you; therefore shall your camp be holy that He may see no shameful thing in you and turn away from you" (Deuteronomy 23:15).

Should uncircumcised warriors be included in Israel's fighting forces, the attribute of Justice intervenes: "No difference exists between both camps. Both have an uncircumcised (unsubmissive) heart and uncircumcised flesh. Only one is larger than the other. Why should the few conquer the many, against the laws of nature?" But when the Israelites are circumcised, the attribute of Justice is silenced, and the attribute of Mercy gains the ascendancy to plead, "Have mercy on Your children who have sealed a covenant with You, and do not deliver them into the hands of their enemies!"

When Yehoshua led the people of Israel across the waters of the Jordan, he did not begin the war of conquest till he had circumcised all those who had been born in the wilderness (they had not been properly circumcised because of the harsh desert conditions). This was done so that the Israelites should know that not by the sword would they gain possession of the land, but rather through the strength of the Almighty and the merit of their observance of the covenant.

HERITAGE AND INHERITANCE

"And I shall give you and your progeny after you the land of your sojourning—the entire land of Canaan—as an everlasting possession; and I shall be God to them." Then God said to Avraham, "On your part, observe My covenant, you and your progeny after you, throughout their generations" (Genesis 17:7-8).

We learn from this that the Israelites were to inherit the land of Canaan from their forebears only by the merit of milah. On this condition was the Land of Israel granted to Avraham; and for this reason did the Holy One command Yehoshua to circumcise the Israelites when they were about to enter the land (Midrash Aggadah).

HONOR IN PLACE OF SHAME

"This is My covenant which you shall keep, between Me and you and your progeny after you: every male among you shall be circumcised" (Genesis 17:10).

It is written, "and Your Torah is within my innards" (Psalms 40:9): How fortunate are the Israelites that they have a mitzvah concerning every limb and part! For example, concerning the head there is the mitzvah, "You shall not round the corners of your heads . . . " (Leviticus 19:27); pertaining to the flesh, "You shall not make any cuts in your flesh . . . " (Leviticus 19:28). Likewise do we have the mitzvah of milah, "you are to circumcise the flesh of your foreskins . . ." (Genesis 17:11).

The purpose of these mitzvoth is to give a man the means to gain control over his entire body, directing every limb and part toward the service of God (Yalkut Shimoni, Judges 42).

[Judasim does not idealize, for that means distortion and escape from reality. Rather, it sanctifies—which implies direct confrontation with a lower reality with the aim of raising it to a more spiritual and creative plane. An example of this can be seen in Judaism's attitude towards sex, which, rather than being one of denial or contempt, is one of acceptance together with the requirement that man express this (as well as every other) facet of himself, in a sanctified system. Furthermore, precisely because this instinct is so strong, does it provide man with the greater challenge of sanctifying himself through it.]*

The organ of reproduction need not be a source of sin, as man can utilize his freedom to raise *every* aspect of life to a higher level. God manifested His love for Avraham by giving him this opportunity through the covenant of milah. And furthermore, when man overcomes his strongest

* Translator's note.

passion by sanctifying it, he has the power to convert all his other weaker impulses to positive ones.

"All my bones shall say: HA-SHEM, who is like You?" (Psalms 35:10). Said David: I praise you with all my limbs and parts, as I observe mitzvoth with them: . . . the nails, to do the *pri'ah* with them* . . . the knees, on which, when I am the *sandek*, I place the children for their milah . . . (Yalkut Shimoni on Psalms, 723).

Through milah, Avraham became whole and complete as an *olah*, an offering burned in its entirety on the altar. No areas or parts of shame were left, as every part of his body was sanctified with the mitzvoth.

THREE SIGNS

Of the six hundred and thirteen commandments in the Torah, only three were designated as *signs*: the Sabbath, tefillin (phylacteries) and circumcision.

Concerning the Sabbath the Torah writes, "It is an eternal *sign* between Me and the children of Israel; for in six days the Lord made heaven and earth, and on the seventh day He ceased working and rested" (Exodus 31:12).

Concerning tefillin the Torah says, "And it shall be for you as a *sign* upon your hand and a remembrance between your eyes, in order that HA-SHEM's Torah may be in your mouths, for with a mighty hand HA-SHEM brought you out of Egypt" (*ibid.* 13:9).

Concerning milah, the Torah says, ". . . this will be a *sign* of the covenant between Me and you . . . " (Genesis 17:11).

Three signs—three testimonies.

The sign of the Sabbath testifies to the Almighty's omnipotence and force which moves all of creation. He works and rests at will; His creations must work or rest at

* *Pri'ah*: slitting and drawing back the membrane, to leave the corona uncovered.

His command. Thus, by observing the Sabbath, man acknowledges the Almighty's ultimate authority: that there is no Creator or Builder but He, and no creation or formation but through His will.

The sign of tefillin testifies to the Almighty's power and providence in history. It is God who grants superiority to some nations over others. The Jewish people are thus commanded to wear tefillin on the left—the weaker—hand, in order to acknowledge that it was God's hand and not theirs which rescued them from Egypt.

The sign of the covenant of milah testifies to the Almighty's power over life's processes and realities. There is no dualism between body and soul, heaven and earth, light and dark—all are part of a single entity, ruled by one Power. The totality of a man's thoughts and desires are rooted in one source: they are God's works and their ultimate purpose is to serve Him. Moreover, in a paradoxical manner, praise which issues from a lower realm is even greater than prayerful adoration which comes from a higher sphere: the praise of HA-SHEM that comes from the darkness of the body and its desires is even greater than what pours forth from the soul!

The creatures of the higher celestial spheres open in praise and hymn, while the lowest of creatures in the depths of earthliness answer, and all join in unison, "Holy, holy, holy is HA-SHEM of hosts, His grandeur fills the earth!"

The blood of milah symbolizes man's exaltation and ascendancy through his control over his lower bodily forces.

THE GREATNESS OF THE MITZVAH

Rabbi Yishmael said: Great is the mitzvah of milah, for thirteen covenants were made over it [the term "covenant" is used thirteen times in the Torah's passage about milah] (Rashi, Nedarim 31).

These thirteen covenants allude to the thirteen

attributes of Divine mercy [for God revealed these attributes of mercy as a reward for the mitzvah of milah] (Rabbi Yaakov Emden, *Migdal Oz*).

Rabbi Yose says: Great is the mitzvah of milah, for it supersedes the severe laws of the Sabbath* (Nedarim 31).

Rabbi Yehoshua ben Korcha says: Great is milah, for all Moshe's merits did not protect him when he delayed keeping this mitzvah" ** (*ibid.*).

Great is milah, for without it the world could not endure (*ibid.*).

Great is milah, for the Almighty swore to Avraham that anyone who is circumcised will not endure Gehinnom (Midrash Tanchuma on *Lech Lecha*, 20).

Great is milah, for a child does not enter in the reckoning of the generations unless he is circumcised (Midrash).

Even if they have no righteous deeds to their credit, the Almighty will redeem the Jewish people in the merit of milah (Aggadath Bereshith 17).

An uncircumcised person may not study Torah. Akilas, nephew of the Roman Emperor Hadrian, wanted to convert to Judaism, but he feared his uncle. So Akilas asked him, "I want to venture into business, so I want to go abroad and learn how people's minds work. I would like your advice on how to proceed." Hadrian answered, "Engage in any business which seems lowly—as low as the earth—for in the end its status will rise and you will profit." So Akilas came to the Land of Israel, studied Torah, and converted to Judaism. He then returned to his uncle Hadrian. The

* Milah may be performed on the Sabbath, if it is the eighth day of the infant's life, although this bit of surgery would ordinarily be a desecration of the Sabbath, punishable by death.

** The reference is to Exodus 4:24. The Sages explain that he was in danger of losing his life because he had thus far failed to circumcise his son (cited in Rashi on the verse).

Emperor asked, "Why is your face altered? Has your business venture failed? Or has someone perhaps harmed you?"

The nephew answered, "No! Nothing like that occurred. I studied Torah and circumcised myself."

"And who advised you so?" asked the emperor.

"I sought your advice," replied Akilas. "You said, engage in any business which seems lowly, as low as the earth, for in the end its status will rise. I traversed all the lands, and nowhere did I see a people as lowly as the Jews; so in the end their status will rise."

"And why did you circumcise yourself?"

"Because I wished to study Torah."

"Well, you should have studied Torah without circumcision!"

Akilas answered, "Would you reveal your confidences to someone who was not utterly devoted to you? Similarly, if a person is not circumcised, he cannot study Torah" (Midrash Tanchuma on *Mishpatim*, 5).

THE JOY OF THE MITZVAH

Rabbi Shimon bar Yochai said: Behold, a man loves no one better than his son, and yet he circumcises him! Rabbi Nachman bar Shmuel added: He does so to do the will of his Maker. He rejoices over the mitzvah even though he sees his son's blood being shed. Rabbi Chanina said: And not only this, but he goes to the expense of making a celebration, which he was not even commanded to do! Moreover, a person will go to lengths to borrow money and buy on credit, in order to make this day a joyous one (Midrash Tanchuma on *Tetzaveh*, 1).

Rabban Shimon the son of Gamliel says: Every mitzvah which was originally accepted joyfully, such as milah, continues to be celebrated joyfully (Shabbath 130).

From this we learn that a man who brings his son to be

circumcised is comparable to a *kohen gadol* (high priest) bringing his offerings to the altar. From this the Sages learned that "a person is obligated to make the day of his son's circumcision one of joy and festivity" (Yalkut Shimoni, 1:81).

And why do we rejoice so much over this mitzvah?

Because it is the first mitzvah a person participates in—when he is only eight days old.

Because it was given to us as a covenantal sign by God.

Because it is a sign which binds the Jew to the covenant all his life, even against his will. The Jew's perpetual prayer is "and do not bring us to a test of temptation": Afraid that he may fail the Almighty's tests, the Jew is joyous that the greatest mitzvah is sealed indelibly, forever.

Because while other mitzvoth are performed only at specified times, this mitzvah is permanent.

Permanent it is indeed—the sign of the unbreakable bond between the Almighty and His people. Through history we have kept this sacred rite, whatever the cost in pain and sacrifice. And in turn He has kept us in existence, as an indestructible moral force, to live on until we reach our ultimate destiny and attain universal recognition as His people.

A mohel's instrument box, of pewter, made in the shape of a cradle, with an incised drawing of a circumcision scene. (Bohemia, 17th-18th century)